THE WORLD IS A BUNDLE OF HAY

THE WORLD IS A BUNDLE OF HAY

ROY ALAN PREECE

SN❄WFLAKE BOOKS LTD

Published by Snowflake Books Ltd.
The Midstall, Randolphs Farm, Hassocks,
West Sussex, BN6 9EL, UK
First published 2013

Cover and text designed by Snowflake Books Ltd.
Illustrations by Roy Alan Preece and Jian Zhi Qiu
Printed in Taiwan by Choice Printing Group
ISBN 978-1-908350-00-8

'If we are to enjoy life to the full we must be aware of the beauty and value of the commonplace, and of the interconnectedness of everything.'

It seemed appropriate to use the traditional measures of feet, yards and miles for this story. For readers who are not familiar with these, one inch is twenty-five millimetres, one foot is about thirty centimetres, one yard is about ninety centimetres, and one mile is a little more than one and a half kilometres. An acre is about half a hectare. One pound weight is about half a kilogram and a ton is about one thousand kilograms. A dozen is the number twelve and was a common traditional base used for counting and calculation.

$\mathcal{X}$

The cover picture is from a painting 'Haymaking' by Joseph Harold Swanwick and is reproduced courtesy of Sotheby's Picture Library.

Henry Fox-Talbot's photograph 'The Hay Stack' is reproduced courtesy of the Science and Society Picture Library of the National Museum of Science and Industry.

The J.H.Palmer & Sons poster 1935 is reproduced by kind permission of Greenslade Taylor Hunt.

$\mathcal{X}$

CONTENTS

1 The Country

Existing precariously between sky and water the Somerset Levels have special qualities. Stamp your foot on the earth in winter or spring and you will feel the ground tremble and hear the water gurgling and undulating all round you, only inches below the surface. Dig a hole – or a grave – more than a foot deep and it will immediately fill with water. The flat land, with few trees other than large hawthorn bushes, may distort your sense of physical proportion so that walking across a twenty acre field with the complete semicircle of sky above, you will sometimes have the curious feeling of being ten feet tall. As the moist air cools on a clear night a vapour grows mysteriously out of the soil, forming a white layer of mist perhaps only two feet deep, obscuring your feet, while above is a bright moon which lights up the surface of the mist with just a hint of the colours of a rainbow; there is a magical feeling that you are walking on a cloud and kicking it away, like autumn leaves, as you walk.[1]

Because of the unseen moisture the air has a soft and somnolent quality; it is mixed with scents of many things: water peppermint, meadowsweet, willow leaves, the chamomile in the stony gateways, the may blossom, the sweet breath of cattle, warm milk; and everywhere the grass and hay. All is lightly salted by the presence of the sea. The senses become confused – that sudden movement of reeds by a breeze: did you hear it or did you smell it? To hear a skylark sing was like a sweet taste on the tongue; working in the fields we would all stop and look up and search for that small speck in the immensity of blue; then someone would shout, 'There he is,' and we would each get on with our job. Why we felt compelled to satisfy ourselves of the bodily source of that singing I don't know, but somehow we felt more contented for it.

My chemistry tutor at university specialised in finding the chemicals that make up the scents of natural things – and, in his spare time, in making a photographic collection of misericords. He told us that behind the principal chemical of a scent there was always another and another, like the harmonies and sub-harmonies of a plucked string, so that he could never reproduce completely a scent in all its subtlety, which is why the scented products that we buy often seem harsh. I wondered what he would make of the smells of our countryside which formed a whole symphony of scents vibrating on the air – very *pianissimo* of course, for the acrid smells of modern intensive farming were not present then. People look at me very oddly when I complain sometimes that the limestone uplands which constitute so much of southern England are dry and have no smell.

With the beauty came hard work. The Levels are threatened by drainage water from the hills to the north – the North Water – and by the sea. Over many centuries men and women have toiled to dig drainage channels, large and small, with various names: gutters, ditches, rhines, pills, cuts, drains; a collective effort which is said to be equal to that of building the pyramids, but which has been far more useful, and yet is unassuming. As Oscar Wilde might have said, how long can you enjoy the contemplation of a pyramid? But the fascination of those quiet watercourses was sufficient for a lifetime.

To make a living out of that watery and vulnerable land was hard work too. My science master, who came from bustling Hertfordshire, used to tell us that Somerset people were very nice, but they were half asleep most of the time. He blamed the air; but perhaps if he had started work at five-thirty in the morning and worked a fourteen-hour day, and seventeen or eighteen at haymaking and harvest, he would have been half asleep. But the people were not in fact sleepy in that way; they had merely learned to pace themselves to the rhythm of their work to get through the long day. Certainly they lived by the maxim of putting off till tomorrow what you don't have to do today, but unfortunately there was a great deal that had to be done every day. Yet they still found time and energy to grow their gardens and to set up many village activities.

Kenneth Galbraith, the American economist, grew up on a farm, as did a number of United States intellectuals; he observed that the good thing about growing up on a farm was that nothing else seemed like hard work ever after.[2] On a Dorsetshire farm where I worked one summer, the cowman started work at four o'clock in the morning; he fed and milked a hundred and twenty cows and sent off the milk by nine o'clock. He had done five hours arduous and continuous work *before breakfas*t. He then helped with farm work all morning and did the second milking in the afternoon. At harvest time he helped with the harvesting until maybe ten o'clock at night. Life was a little easier for the rest of us, although not much, since we started work only at six. That was seven days a week, except that there was no harvesting on Sundays for the farmer belonged to a strict Christian sect.

On the Levels, seventy years ago, it was the best of times and it was not the worst of times. After a century of struggle farm labourers' conditions were fair. Support for agriculture during and after the war gave farmers security and a reasonable prosperity. But at that time our familiar operations and skills had scarcely changed for centuries. Everything was done by muscle power – our own and that of the horses. I still have a rather eccentric idea that to do something by machine and not by hand is somehow unreal. I may not be quite alone, however, in this conceit for there are rich people who will pay large premiums for furniture which is truly handmade. Perhaps we all like to imagine we could survive in a world without machines.

We had two horses: a powerful and temperamental black Shire, called Prince, for heavy work and a smaller and more amenable Bay, Michael, for lighter work. The only external energy we used was the paraffin to light our lamps indoors and our hurricane lamps in the farm buildings, plus some coal for the fire. The grass crop does not suffer much from pests, as arable crops do, so there was no need for pesticides; weeds were controlled by cultivation or by cutting; and such fertilizers as were used were naturally occurring minerals: lime to control soil acidity and, in case of phosphorous deficiency, basic slag, a by-product of the iron industry.

But this largely self-sufficient life was on the cusp of change under the pressures of wartime and afterwards to increase the nation's supply of home-grown food, and by a desire for improved standards of living. Mechanisation and new materials introduced new and somewhat easier ways of doing things. Of course, self-sufficiency was an illusion anyway – it always is. The milk we produced was hauled off by powerful engines to help sustain industrial cities and those cities in turn sustained our nation; and they also provided much that we needed. But such places were largely outside our awareness; we existed mostly in a self-contained cycle which had changed little.

I feel very fortunate to have experienced that life just before it was coming to an end and to have been able to acquire many of its necessary skills. Like Hardy's Egdon Heath, it was and is ballast for the mind. If it was not entirely self-sufficient it was, in the modern jargon, sustainable and therefore, for me at any rate, intensely real and satisfying, whereas a modern large city gives me a deep sense of unreality. My uncle had a small farm which my grandmother had set up for him, partly I think – and who can blame her after the waste and slaughter of the Great War – so that he would not have to be a soldier, since agriculture, like mining, was a protected occupation. At first he employed young trainees from London sent by the Young Men's Christian Association or YMCA who fancied – or perhaps their mentors fancied – they might take to farming. But none of them stayed and as I grew to a useful age it suited him and me that I should became a casual worker for him. For me the arrangement provided a welcome small income, since he paid me at full rates, while giving plenty of time for my studies and a great deal of physical activity and satisfaction and pride in my work as well. For him the advantage was that he gained most of the assistance he needed, but did not have the expense and bother of employing a full-time workman.

The arrangement was flexible, but there were certain obligations, one being that I should always be available for the haymaking each year. I helped with every task from hauling dung onto the fields in winter, and harrowing the pastures in the spring, to mowing, to thatching the ricks and feeding the hay to cattle in the winter. At other times I trimmed field hedges, dug ditches, repaired fencing and renewed gates and gateposts, pollarded the willows, mended farm buildings and carried out basic maintenance on the tractor when my uncle belatedly bought one. I was not so keen on work with the animals, but I could help with a calving or do a milking when he spent a day at the cattle market.

As we worked we often talked, for he was an intelligent man with a deep curiosity.[3] Although he had taken to farming well enough, following his mother's persuasion, it was not the career he had wanted for himself; but my grandmother was a strong-willed matriarch who tried to control all of us by division and by creating mutual and quite unnecessary suspicions. My experience of this has led me to avoid as far as possible all forms of intrigue and situations where intrigue is required. In many ways he was not a typical farmer, although I confess I'm not sure what a typical farmer would be; that acute observer of the countryside, Richard Jeffries, writing in 1880 in *Hodge and his Masters*, argues that: 'In manners, mode of thought, and way of life, there is perhaps no class of the community less uniform than the agricultural. The diversities are so marked as to amount to contradictions.'

Our country had just won a world war and in the process had bankrupted itself, so it was a time of pride combined with austerity; improvisation and the acquisition of second-hand items – greatly assisted by cheap and abundant 'war surplus' – were admirable abilities then and for me still are. Nearly everything manufactured was destined for export; even the rich could not legally buy new cars and when eventually these did become available there was a waiting list of months and no choice of colour. My uncle was especially interested in politics and would often ask me what I thought about this or that thing that the government had done or about the causes

and conduct of the war and of the Cold War. His
accounts of the disastrous inflation in Weimar
Germany made a particular impression on me
and I have had a fear of inflation ever since; I
can never respect any politician who talks of it
lightly. We did not discuss the frivolous topics
that are so much liked in the modern office: there
was no television at first and when it did come
the most exciting thing was whether a certain
Gilbert Harding, dressed in a dinner-jacket of
course, might exhibit a little grumpiness on a
polite quiz show called *What's My Line*; footballers
were modest men who knew how to behave and
earned modest wages; the private lives of film
stars and royalty were discreetly hidden; there
were no pop stars in the modern sense, unless
you count the likeable Vera Lynn or Bing Crosby,
and the iconoclastic Rock and Roll had not yet
arrived. Much more interesting than those sorts
of things were developments in farm machinery
or techniques, the visitations and obtuseness of
agricultural bureaucrats, market prices or the
activities of other farmers past and present.
Occasionally there were dramatic local events
such as rick fires or flooded pastures; and always
worth retelling was the calamitous outbreak
of foot-and-mouth disease in the thirties when

funeral pyres dominated the country and which we thought then we should never see again.[4]

Naturally we talked a good deal about farming activities and how they related to the character of the landscape: how, for example, the heavy clay soils – which could change from being a sticky goo to rock-like lumps in a week – were not really suited to the arable farming which we had been compelled to practise during the war, or at least not with the cultivating power then available. I think that experience explained why my uncle and others did not, as a balanced dairy farm should, grow kale or mangolds as supplementary rations, but bought in modest amounts of concentrated supplements to support milk yields. This did not mean that the fields were mere 'exercising grounds' for supplement-fed animals, as many old pastures had been before the war. On the contrary: the grass and hay crops were well-managed and formed the entire maintenance ration and part of the production ration for the stock.[5]

On this point my uncle delighted in telling of the cows he had owned in the economically depressed period of the nineteen-thirties: animals which would produce long lactations and good milk yields on few or no supplements and which were well-suited to the traditional practice, which he favoured, of low-input-low-output farming. The key to survival in the 'thirties was to minimize outgoing expenditure, a principle which persisted with him even in better times. While the Friesian breed, which became popular with progressive farmers and advisers after the war, produced higher yields, they required a corresponding higher level of feeding and he always argued that they would not have been capable of supporting him under those more difficult conditions. I sometimes wondered whether this was a romantic nostalgia on his part, but eighteenth century writers describe breeds – or rather local types – of cow, such as the Suffolk Dun, that were noted for their good production of milk from plain fodder. There was a poignancy in all this for he treated his cows almost as pets – he always called them ladies – and it had been a great blow to him when he had been required to assist as they were killed and incinerated in that outbreak of foot-and-mouth disease. In a sense this event represented the end of the heroic stage of his farming career.

He was a good judge of milking cattle and bought whatever he thought would do well, whatever its colour, although he favoured Dairy Shorthorn characteristics and most of his cows were roans or brindles (that is flecked with white or grey) of various shades from red to blue, purple or black. There were also a couple of black and white Friesians to boost yields, a placid cream-coloured Guernsey to raise the butterfat average, a hardy red and white Ayrshire from Scotland and even a brick-coloured Red Poll, another adaptable but uncommon breed. He liked to observe and compare their qualities. They were all individuals and to a modern eye would have lacked a desirable uniformity, but we rather liked the picturesque variety; they all had horns of course. The cows certainly were not pedigree stock and some were cross-bred; maybe they had the genes of some of those old breeds which unfortunately had been allowed to become extinct. Now, in the twenty-first century, there is a renewed interest in the sustainability qualities of traditional breeds of farm animal as well as a feeling that the pursuit of very high milk yields is a cruel practice.

These cows produced the milk and the calves which together were the sole source of income for the farm and accordingly they were always treated well. They in turn depended for their existence almost entirely on the grass of the fields and on the hay which was made from it, so that the quality and quantity of production were largely controlled by the management of the grass and its successful conservation as high quality hay. Anyone who has attempted to do a practical job properly or to invent something that works will understand that there are refinements and subtleties – and satisfactions – involved which are not immediately obvious, rather as in the game of cricket. We analysed our tasks: how they were done and why, how they used to be done and how other people did them. Many of these refinements had a practical purpose; others were employed to demonstrate perfect control and neatness and accuracy in what was being done, or to add interest and satisfaction to what would otherwise have been repetitive jobs; and there was always a satisfaction in impressing other farmers.

Because of the curious local pattern of land ownership our work was usually open to public gaze. It was good when someone said, 'That's a neat job,' and not as nice to hear, 'He made a funny job of that'. The tools we used were products of long evolution, in some cases to near perfection. There were right ways and wrong ways to handle them and sharpen them safely and effectively. When some years later I taught myself wood turning there were many books with fine photos and pretty designs, but only one that I know of where the author (F. Pain) seemed to stand beside me and suggest that I held the chisel just so to sharpen it; or that the fast-revolving timber would react to the chisel in such a way; and above all not to scrape the wood thoughtlessly, but to cut intelligently. Traditional farm work needed to be considered in a similarly intelligent way.

✣2 The Grass✣

'Make hay while the sun shines,' advises the old saying – which suggests that it is a good thing to be making hay and that you must do it while you can. Like much traditional wisdom, this proverb has lost its original force and meaning for most of us today, living as we do in a cushioned and opportunistic age. But the great struggle to make and store sufficient hay to feed farm and draft animals throughout the winter months has been a crucial part of sustainable farming and the foundation of national economies in northern Europe for centuries. Hay is only dried grass; yet that word 'only' is misleading, for to preserve large quantities of dried grass for many months and perhaps years required traditional skills, many of which are now forgotten.

We may think we live in an iron age, a coal age, a plastics age or even an atomic age, but our civilisation is still based essentially on grass and on the large family of plants which botanists call the grasses, or the *Graminae*. In this group of plants are found all our cereals – wheat, barley, oats and rye – and these have been developed

by selection from natural grass ancestors which
grew in the wilds of Asia Minor only a few
thousand years ago and which may still be found
there as extreme rarities; by analysing the genes
of modern varieties these ancestors can be
reconstructed. Even the exotic rice plant which
forms the basic diet of half the world's population
is in this wider sense a grass. So too is the corn
or maize plant which supported the ancient
civilisations of Central America although in this
case, uniquely and strangely, no wild ancestor
has ever been found. The bamboo plant which is
used for many traditional crafts and constructions
in the East is a grass. So also is the sugar cane
which was the basis of the economies of the West
Indies until the European Union forced us to use
French sugar beet instead. Most of the animals
which provide our meat, milk, cheese and eggs
have traditionally been fed on grass, hay, grain or
straw. Bread, pastry, pasta and spaghetti are all
made from cereals. The world does indeed seem
to be a bundle of grass, if not always of hay.

Lord Byron wrote in a short poem that, 'The
world is a bundle of hay, and mankind the asses
that pull'. Did he mean 'pull' as when a donkey
pulls a cart of hay or some other burden? Or did
he picture an animal using its mouth to pull out

its sustenance from a bundle of hay? Perhaps he meant both; for while we must serve the grass for a year, it then, like some ancient Minoan king, is sacrificed for us. The main character of this story is the grass; it is my task to tell it, but it is not my story.

Farming on the Somerset plains seventy years ago was a microcosm of a larger world. It was a pastoral grassland economy where the fortunes of human families ebbed and flowed and ultimately depended on how well the grass grew each spring and summer.

Over his desk our woodwork master had an old carved plaque which, from my memory, read something like: *'O waes hael Somer-saetan'*. We didn't know whether it was good Anglo-Saxon or not, but he told us that it meant 'Oh the green hills of Somerset'. (An expert in Anglo-Saxon tells me it probably was meant to say 'Greetings – or good health – Summer-settlers'.) The master further told us that the name Somerset meant 'land of the summer people' and that many years ago its inhabitants would retreat each winter to live on the surrounding hills – the Mendips, the

Quantocks and the Poldens – when the low-lying central plain experienced its annual flooding. We could understand that, for it still flooded then, although not perhaps as badly, despite hundreds of years of drainage works which had been started by the Abbots of the rich Abbey of Glastonbury and carried on more recently and more prosaically by the Somerset Drainage Board.

When the spring returned and the waters receded and the soft peats and sticky clays were firm enough to bear the weight of their animals' hooves, the summer people would migrate from the hills to spend the summer fattening their small flocks and herds on the free and abundant grasses and herbs under those wide and spacious skies which only flatlands can offer. We can imagine these people finding their old camp-sites from the years before; perhaps they made temporary shelters from the pliant and sweet-smelling white willows and from the reeds which are still used for thatching today. It seems likely that it would have been a happy time with young animals and milk and meat in good supply. The herdsmen, like herdsmen everywhere, would be content to see their animals regaining condition and fattening on the lush grasses after the privations of winter. Such seasonal migrations are what geographers like to call *transhumance*. The best-known example of this process occurs in the Swiss Alps where animals and people move up to the high mountain pastures each spring once the snows have melted.

Within this winter sea, however, were islands on which settlements developed. Some of these islands were natural outliers of the rocks of the surrounding hills. Some are still locally called 'isles' today – although they are no longer true islands – and official maps used to name them as such. There is the Isle of Wedmore where King Alfred signed his famous treaty with the Dane, Guthrum, and so established Anglo-Saxon rule in what is now southern England, and Christianity everywhere. The less prominent Isle of Athelney was where Alfred had earlier hidden himself throughout one perilous winter as the invading Danes rampaged over the whole country, while Anglo-Saxon control was for a time reduced to these few small acres protected by the flooded reedy marshland. The most famous island among all these is the Isle of Glastonbury with its impressive and evocative ruined abbey. Glastonbury is sometimes named on maps as the Isle of Avalon because of its supposed association with the fabled King Arthur. The Tor of Glastonbury, a medieval church tower without a church, set on a conical hill, can be seen from miles around in the flat landscape as an evocative symbol of the past.

On the marshes themselves and well over two thousand years ago other, artificial, islands were laboriously constructed, presumably for security: these were the now famous Lake Villages with their associated secret trackways and their punt-shaped boats dug out of solid tree-trunks. Outlines of these villages and their huts can still be seen faintly on the face of the land and their boats and other things in local museums. Perhaps they represented early attempts to live on the marshes all year round, or they may suggest that there were disputes over the land each summer; it is possible that the times were not so idyllic after all. But as the drainage improved and floods became less prolonged, individual farmsteads were set up and life became more settled, though there were still vestiges of transhumance to be found in the farming of seventy years ago.

As well as the major drainage courses, 'pills' and 'rhines' of the strategic schemes, minor ditches were dug to define field boundaries as enclosures took place over the centuries, while in the fields themselves systems of small gutters were also dug out, all forming a networked system in the continual fight to avoid being overwhelmed by the water, and in total representing an enormous task of manual labour. As bushes and trees established themselves informally along the banks of the drainage channels the familiar and historical landscape of the Somerset Levels was formed. It seems strange to me to write about fields for we always called these enclosed areas 'grounds', whether in specific names such as Home Ground, Moor Ground or Square Ground or as a general term. The word comes from the Old English *'grund'* meaning surface of the earth, especially as distinct from the sky, and perhaps its use reflects a consciousness of that vulnerable and precious surface between air and water.

A farmer or smallholder sitting in church or chapel on a June Sunday seventy years ago, scrubbed and self-conscious, would have his mind on his grass, cut and drying in one of his grounds (or fields), and his eye on the sky outside, wondering whether the weather would stay fine tomorrow. The doings of the ancient Hebrews, with their flocks and herds and pastures, as read out perhaps in the first lesson from the Old

Testament, would seem very real to him. The
beautiful poetry of the Authorized Version of
The Bible would have great poignancy: 'As for
man, his days are as grass: as a flower of the field,
so he flourisheth'.

Why, you may wonder, were those farmers in
church while the sun was shining, and not outside
making hay? Seventy years ago and for long
before that, especially in country areas, there was
a strong sabbatarian feeling. 'Six days shalt thou
labour…' and on the seventh rest; the ancient Ten
Commandments were, even now, written on the
chancel wall in front of their eyes.

Some from conviction, most perhaps from
social or family pressure, would not like to be
seen carrying out unnecessary work on a Sunday.
Of course cows had to be milked and animals
fed, but only an un-godly fringe would harvest
on a Sunday. The convention was strongest
among the nonconformists: the Methodists and
Baptists; the West Country had long been stoutly
nonconformist. But ever since Queen Elizabeth
the First had required everyone to attend Church
on Sundays, that compulsion was also felt by
Anglicans. The larger farmers were the leaders
in the local community and a popular vicar could
deploy moral and social pressures on them,

and especially on their wives, to attend church although the proscription against actual labour was not as strong among Anglicans.

The custom of church attendance was justified in various ways quite apart from edicts of God or Queen; in true protestant fashion, reasons were sought. It was argued that God looked after the righteous, although a study of that same bible and not least the story of Job did not in truth support this naïve idea. Maybe if the righteous appeared to prosper it was because they were careful about where they spent their money. Then there was the opposite argument of Divine punishment. A man in the village had been knocking down an old wall one Sunday morning; it fell on him and killed him. He left behind a wife and two young children. 'There,' it was whispered, 'he was working on the Sabbath!' It seemed a harsh Old Testament God who would punish a widow and orphans for the supposed sins of their man, yet it was surprising how many apparently kindly people held this view. The idea was reinforced by myth; children were taught that the old man in the moon, whose face we can all see when the moon is full, was banished there because he had gathered sticks for his fire on a Sunday.

There was another side to this argument

of course. In a time when labour was long and hard and holidays few, the restriction on Sunday working was a welcome relief: if not for the farmer worried about his hay, then certainly for his workers. That the Sabbath was made for man and not man for the Sabbath had a different resonance in harder and simpler times. Some workers, supposedly because of their religious beliefs, would refuse to work on a Sunday, except to provide necessary care for the animals. Some farmers would not employ such a person. Others, however, might prefer someone who shared their beliefs and who would not expect extra overtime on Sundays. Robert Stevenson, grandfather of Robert Louis Stevenson, experienced similar problems among his Calvinistic workmen when building the famous Bell Rock lighthouse, though every day of fine weather and hour of low tide was precious if the work was to be made secure before the next storm.

These arguments, for most people at least, seem arcane today and such a society may appear to have been intolerant. Yet the very fact of these differences existing side by side demonstrates that in a deeper sense the society was tolerant; no one was persecuted for their beliefs and, while birds of the same feather generally flocked together, in an emergency anyone would be helped. But these differences were important then: they could determine employment; they influenced who mixed with whom; and sometimes they determined when the hay would be 'got in'.

So the farmer of seventy years ago would have mixed feelings, veering from righteousness to rebellion, as he sat in church on a fine day, watching the dancing golden daylight cooled and stilled by the stained glass of the slender windows, vaguely aware that he was part of a tradition that stretched back in time hundreds or maybe thousands of years. Neither he nor anyone could have foreseen that in a generation many of his skills would be obsolete. His mind would be on the more immediate future – would Monday bring a week of fine weather or of bad?

Farming textbooks describe haymaking as an uncertain process although the aims are easily stated. It is to dry the grass quickly so that its nutrient value is preserved and to achieve just that moisture content at which it will neither rot in storage nor, more dramatically, overheat and burst into flames. When the weather is exceptionally fine – as in a period of heat wave or a 'real haymaker' – three days might be sufficient. The grass is mown the first day, starting early in the morning, and lies under the intense heat of the sun for most of that day so that by the evening the process of drying is well begun. Sometime the next day it will be judged fit for 'turning'; the neat rows of drying grass are turned over, either by hand or by machine, so that the still-green underside is now exposed. Late on the third day it may be ready for 'carrying' to be formed into a rick in a corner of the ground or for 'loading' on to wagons to be transported to the farmyard. This was a laborious and time-consuming process and perhaps would run into a fourth day. Conditions are rarely as ideal as this however. Often damp cloudy weather intervenes, or even days of heavy rain. The green grass fails to 'turn' colour into golden hay and may even begin to rot where it lies. One day's delay before the fine weather breaks up may result in a lost week or even a lost crop. The fickleness of the English summer weather is well-known.

The critical point – the bottleneck – in livestock farming is always the late winter: has enough fodder been stored to feed the animals through this period when grass does not grow because of the cold? Our history books used to say glibly that in the Middle Ages all the animals had to be killed in the autumn because of lack of winter fodder. No doubt beasts that were in any case to be slaughtered for meat would be best killed at the end of the autumn grazing season and their meat salted down or dried. But when it is remembered that a cow carries her calf in her womb for about as long as a human mother, three-quarters of a year, and that a heifer or young cow would not breed until nearly two years old, and that a cow rarely has more than one calf, then simple arithmetic shows that many cattle needed to be fed through the winter if the herd was to survive. Then there were the highly trained horses of the rich and the shared draught-oxen of the poor, although admittedly the survival of the peasants' more prolific and omnivorous pigs would be less dependent on stored supplies.

Seventy or eighty years ago it was the dried grass, the hay, which provided the major part of the store of winter fodder in the low-input-low-output sustainable farming system that was practised on the Somerset Plain. Agriculture is the wonderful process of the trapping and harnessing of the energy of the sun to make food. This is truly 'solar energy' although we tend to think of that now only in terms of electricity production. It is not of course the energy used to dry the hay that is mainly important, but the capture and storage of energy during the plant's growth through the natural process of photosynthesis: literally 'building up from light'. In twenty-first century agriculture on the other hand it has been said that more energy is sometimes put in as fuel and chemicals than the energy value of the food which is produced.

In the 1930s, during the agricultural depression following the end of the First World War, the economics of agriculture were marginal. Many farmers turned to dairying precisely because the inputs were low and because the government's Milk Marketing Board ensured a regular market and payment for their product. The watery grasslands of the Somerset Plain where 'the grass always grows'[6] were ideal for this enterprise, but even so the margins between survival and bankruptcy were thin. A farmer who found he did not have sufficient hay to see him through the winter would be forced either to sell some animals at this time when prices would be low or to buy hay at a high price. He might try to 'take up', that is to borrow, money from a bank or more likely from a solicitor to tide him over, but that would just increase his outgoings and if the spring was late that year and the grass did not grow on time he would be deeper into difficulty.

As I am writing this I have just read that the weather in 2010 has caused a hay and straw shortage; that hay prices are up by twenty to forty per cent; that theft of hay is an increasing problem and that hay prices might increase by fifty per cent by the beginning of 2011. A radio item has recounted how a dairy farmer in Kent has been put out of business because the unusually dry summer meant there was no grass in the fields for his cows and he was forced to use up his store of the silage (another form of conserved grass) intended for the coming winter. With insufficient feed for the winter he sensibly quit before getting deeper into trouble. It would not have been an easy decision to give up a whole way of life.

Having neglected its farmers and relied on imported food, Britain had found itself in a very serious situation during the Second World War when German U-boats were sinking large numbers of merchant ships. After the war the government this time adopted a policy of agricultural support. Farmers used to say the two best things that happened to British agriculture were Adolf Hitler and Tom Williams, the minister who brought in the support policy. Even so, the habits of careful husbandry, parsimony even, persisted. The farmer in church would doubtless

some time have heard the biblical parable of the
wise and foolish virgins: those who had made sure
they had sufficient oil for their lamps and those
who had not. He would want to have sufficient
hay.

However, for the milking-cows brought into
sheds for the winter, the hay would need to be
supplemented in some way. This might be with the
more juicy goodness of mangolds or turnips: root
crops developed by eighteenth century pioneers
of agriculture such as 'Turnip' Townsend,
the Earl of Leicester. Alternatively (and more
conveniently, since the turnips would have to be
cultivated as as an arable crop) some 'concentrates'
might be bought in the form of pressed 'cake'
from oilseed processing; but hay was still the
staple feed both in cheapness and quantity. Young
animals which were not yet productive were often
fed only on hay, together with such vegetation as
they could scavenge in the fields where they were
pastured through the cold winter months with
little shelter.

Our farmer in church may have cut his grass
yesterday or the day before and is now thinking
he should be turning it today. Or perhaps he
turned it yesterday and would like to be loading
it now because he fears the weather will be wet

tomorrow. Maybe he is expecting a few days of settled weather and wishes he could gain a day by being out mowing instead of sitting through a church service. But, despite religion and weather, there was always enough determination to make sure the hay was made.

☙3 The Ricks❧

Where to begin? The farming year is a cycle which runs on from generation to generation. The whirling 'Dancing Dervishes' of Arabia speak of the still centre of their turning circle, but that is an inward looking and static vision. I prefer to think of the remarkable fact that for any moving wheel, whatever its speed, the point on its circumference, the rim that touches the earth is, *for a moment*, stationary. If there is a time when a farmer is especially conscious that part of the great wheel of nature which is the farming cycle seems to pause and kiss the earth, it is surely in the autumn. Between the dawn to dusk activity of summer and the uncertainties of winter, the autumn was a time of consolidation and satisfaction.

For a cereal farmer the great expression of the year's effort and skill was his huge corn stacks. For the livestock farmer his pride was and still is in his animals, but his hayricks were also a source of satisfaction and display; they were, too, a sort of credit rating which proclaimed his ability to get through the winter. Traditionally in England autumn is the time for flower and vegetable shows when 'five onions' or 'three roses' and many other items which have been carefully grown and selected by gardeners are displayed to best advantage in attempts to win jealously sought prizes. Similarly a farmer would prepare his main ricks, those in his farmyard, to look their best. Some of this preparation was necessary to enable the rick to survive the attacks of time and weather, but in many farm operations, as in flower shows, there were arbitrary standards set which went beyond simple usefulness; these standards seem to have been a way of imparting pride and interest into what was basically, after all, hard manual labour.

The mid-September sky was blue as a clutch of song thrush's eggs. The fierce heat of the summer had passed, but the sun still glowed very warm and golden so that even the shadows seemed full of light. Every surface was dry and welcoming to the touch: the rounded grey lias stones of the farmyard floor, worn smooth by iron-bonded wagon wheels and by the iron-shod hooves of horses; the wood of the cowshed; the sharp-smelling metal of the tools; and the earth itself; while the new haystack on which we were to work spread its sweet scent of coumarin over all.

At that time of year more than any other there was a bodily affinity with the physical world; there was delight in every contact, whether it was the rough sweet-smelling coil of sisal rope on my shoulder, the work-worn handles of the peaks, the touch of hot October sun on our foreheads, or the dry dust which lay between the warm stones. The hectic but enjoyable days of summer haymaking were over; the seemingly endless muddy round of winter yet to come. Those autumn days were deeply satisfying.

As far as I know you will not see a traditional hay or corn rick anywhere in Britain now; corn is threshed in combine harvesters immediately as it is cut; straw and grass are baled by machines. In old haymaking prints and scenes such as you may still find on a cottage wall or, more likely now, in an antique shop, hayricks are shown as rather shapeless rounded masses. This apparent shapelessness may be because these scenes often are of 'Haymaking' taking place; ricks in the process of being built did get rather untidy.

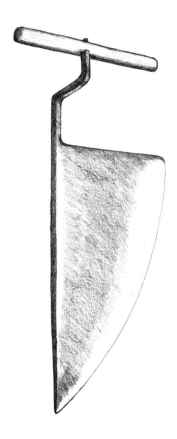

Hay Knife

Hayricks were made either round, square or rectangular in plan, but in our part of England the rectangular shape was most usual; I think this may have been because small adjustments were necessary each year to accommodate how heavy or light the grass crop was and this adjustment was more easily done with a rectangular shape; the geometry of circles is more complex. It was also easier to control the shape of a squarish rick while it was being built.

The rarely made round ricks were considered to need exceptional skill in building but, in our world at least, were felt to be perhaps a little 'showy'. So our ricks when thatched looked like rectangular cottages and in old photographs it is sometimes difficult to tell which is which. 'Pulling the rick' was the operation which turned those rough shaggy sides into vertical flat walls of tightly packed and weatherproof hay.

In the autumn sunshine we gathered together a number of traditional tools, most of which are now seen only in museums or perhaps rotting and rusting away in a corner of a modern farmyard.[7] First was a hay knife whose main use was in the winter for cutting out blocks or 'tods' of hay from the rick. It had a wide flat blade which curved convexly down from a width of about ten inches to a point; the back of the blade was straight and continued up into a vertical iron bar which was bent at the top to get the handle out of the plane of the blade and then topped with a horizontal wooden handle. It was used with a pumping action, up and down. The bend or 'crank' in the handle was necessary so that successive cuts could be truly vertical while the handle – and our knuckles – stayed clear of the previously cut surface above. It was heavy, tall as a young child and it was kept razor sharp. As children we were allowed to use many dangerous implements which would horrify today's authorities, but this hay knife was absolutely forbidden to us then. To handle it now was a mark of growing up.

Another essential tool, widely used in haymaking, was a wooden hay rake. Its back was a slender piece of wood about a yard in length; into this back were fixed wooden peg teeth, each about six inches long. The handle was a slender piece of round ash wood, split and splayed out at the bottom where it too was fixed to the back. To use this tool was a delight: light and simple in construction, yet strong if used properly; that meant never thrusting it out horizontally like an iron garden rake and dragging it forward; the teeth would break instantly as they snagged on

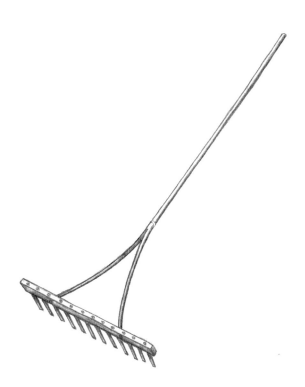

Hay Rake

the ground. The handle had to be held almost vertically, passing over one shoulder, so that the teeth were nearly horizontal as they were drawn over the rough surface; hands were placed rather as for playing a cello. The splayed handle, as well as giving rigidity to the join with the head, allowed a large bundle of hay to be dragged towards the user; some rakes had a light frame attached especially for this function. It was considered a shameful error to break a tooth. Even when used properly a tooth might dig into a clod of earth so that using this rake demanded a carefully calibrated mix of force and delicacy such as few tools require today.

A fearsome and rather rare instrument was the 'gurt ir'n tuth rake'. Anything unusually strong or large was called 'gurt' in Somerset dialect. This 'iron tooth' rake was quite the opposite of the wooden rake: made entirely of iron and with long curved pointed teeth resembling fangs, it was almost indestructible. It had few uses and generally one rake was shared among several neighbours, although who actually owned it was never clear. Then there was the 'wagon line', a very long, one inch diameter rope (sailors would call it a three inch rope from its circumference) of natural fibre. This was long enough to pass several times over and around a fully loaded wagon of hay.

Three hay picks, which we usually called 'peaks' locally, were needed; two were standard length, that is about five feet, and one was extra long, about seven feet or more, and known as a pitching peak. This was used for lifting or 'pitching' hay up onto a tall rick. The smaller peaks were all beautifully crafted in their construction: light and well-balanced so that in use we scarcely noticed their weight and, as with all good tools, they seemed like extensions of oneself, unlike the clumsy 'designer made' tools of today. Being

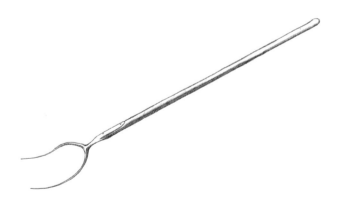

Hay Peak

handmade there were subtle differences in their feel and we each had our favourite. Since the design and use of the peak are so important in haymaking perhaps they may be described now.

The metal part of a hay peak was a marvel of the ironmaster's art and skill in moulding, casting and tempering material. Most peaks had two slender tines or prongs; a very few, usually favoured by beginners, had three, for at first sight it seems impossible to pick up loose wispy hay on two slender prongs set wide apart. With experience, however, people soon graduated to two. These varieties were identified as 'two sprung' and 'three sprung' peaks. There were also four sprung models, but those were used mainly for moving dung or manure and were stronger and not as elegant as the hay forks. I don't know whether the term 'sprung' comes from 'prong' or from 'spring'; perhaps it is a mixture of both: a 'springy prong'. For springy they certainly were and maybe 'sprung' here means 'made springy' for the iron was beautifully tempered by the foundry. Like all good highly tempered tools, the prongs would break before they would bend, but they withstood a good deal of rough use and breakages were extremely rare. I have an old peak in front of me now; the handle has long rotted away and the iron is pitted with rust, yet if I strike the prongs they still vibrate as does a tuning fork and when I place the stem on a wooden table the wood sounds and sings in sympathy. I don't think that any such fine tools are made now.

This one is a three sprung: the central prong is twelve inches long; the outer ones are longer overall since they curve out at first, sideways from the base. In order to reduce weight the prongs are not round or square, but are oval in section, for the iron is made thicker where the greatest stress occurs in use. Like a horizontal branch of a tree, which naturally grows thicker on its under surface to support its weight, the prongs have been thickened along their upper and lower surfaces the better to support the weight of the hay. Perhaps thickened gives the wrong impression for the prongs have a slender character and it may be more correct to say they have been slimmed down at their sides where strength is not so necessary. Their cross-section is not in fact truly oval, but is the shape of the area formed by two intersecting circles, with acute angles at top and bottom to make best use of the tensile and compressive strength of the iron. To speak of the prongs being attached to the central base is misleading for they flow and diminish organically from the base in a single casting, as does a tree trunk from the earth: base and prong are a unity. In this example, the prong, just after it has left the base, is three eighths of an inch in depth and only one quarter of an inch wide; halfway along its length it is a quarter of an inch deep and a mere three sixteenths wide; one inch from its point it is three sixteenths deep and an amazing only one eighth of an inch wide. The subtlety and affinity with natural form shown in designing and casting such a fine implement are impressive, but there is more.

The nineteenth century writer and art critic John Ruskin searched for the perfect curved line; living in a Romantic age he naturally sought this line in nature rather than in geometry and thought he had found it in Alpine scenery, in the curve of a small glacier near Chamonix. Ruskin thought the perfect curve would comprise a gently curving slope terminating in and balanced by a more abrupt curve. The prongs of a hay peak seen from the side have just such a curve; whether it is perfect I don't know, but it is beautiful and it is also practical. It may be thought of rather as the opposite of Ruskin's ideal in that it begins with a sharp curve originating from the base and blending into a shallower curve which is not so much a termination, but rather gives a suggestion of the line continuing unseen. Perhaps it is not quite as complete as Ruskin would have liked.

When hay is carried with the peak handle held horizontally the upward curve in the prongs helps to prevent the hay sliding off; anyone who compared this in use with the straight tines of a garden fork would soon discover the convenience of the traditional design; but to be fair, since the garden forks are intended mostly for digging they need to be straight, like a spade. Then as the hay is being deposited the peak handle is at the same time rotated through one hundred and eighty degrees so that the prongs point downwards and the hay slides smoothly off the slender prongs. 'Turn your peak' was the cry to beginners in the hayfield who did not yet comprehend this trick; it becomes a natural movement after a time. Another advantage of the varied degree of curvature is that when the handle of a peak is held comfortably at waist height with the curved backs of the prongs resting on the ground, the straighter parts of the prongs will be more or less horizontal and the hay can then be gathered up conveniently by sliding the prongs forward along the surface.

Seeing, but perhaps not always understanding, beautiful tools such as the hay peak (the axe was the favourite example) modern designers developed the slogan 'Form follows function', with the implication that something that has been designed purely for its use will also be beautiful. There are several flaws in this argument, which are too many to deal with here. Often traditional tools which are clearly designed for a specific function are not in fact *well*-designed, but are clumsy and inelegant, though they may possess a rustic charm to the modern person who does not have to work with them; beauty only follows function where there is an intimate understanding, developed over many years, of the relation between the form and action of the human body and natural materials. Modern designers, however, then go on to make an illogical perversion of this argument by asserting that anything which is functional must therefore be beautiful. The 'form follows function' assertion has been used as a mendacious justification for the production of much modern ugliness and I would not want this analysis of the hay peak to be used in support of it.

Pulling was literally that: we grasped handfuls of hay from the sides of the rick and pulled them out. If there were many thistles in the hay I wore a leather glove. It was a matter of pride to develop hard hands through working, but mine never became tough enough to grasp a bunch of dried thistles. The loose hay we were pulling out would have deteriorated through the winter, not having the protection of being closely packed. Very loose parts we dressed down first with the wooden rake, or the iron rake even might be used on a more solid bulge or a part that was 'a bit heavy', but we had to be careful not to rake out too much and end up with a hollow instead. Whether standing on the ground or on a ladder to reach the higher parts, we always pulled downwards; in that way the whole shaggy coat of the rick was brushed downwards and would shed rain in the same way as an animal's coat does. The aim was to produce a flat vertical surface overall, so a good 'eye' was necessary, glancing left and right to make sure everything was even, pulling perhaps more here and less there. Some people built their ricks with the sides leaning outward slightly which must have been even more resistant to the weather, but this shape was not as easy to control during building and was more often used for corn ricks where each individual sheaf could be placed precisely. A large round rick, as discussed above, together with outward sloping sides displayed the height of a rick builder's skill. Ricks like this are shown in Claude Monet's series of painting studies in which he set out to record the effects of weather and time on the hayrick and its endurance, but his ricks seem to be quite small. These paintings, incidentally, while not as famous as his water lilies, are possibly more evocative and deserve to be better known.

Was all this care we took to produce a flat surface really necessary? Maybe bulges or hollows could cause a diversion of the smooth flow of rain down the sides, allowing it to enter the rick, but undoubtedly the work was done largely in order to impress. Most farmsteads were situated beside the roads for this was a causeway village, grown up on a narrow ridge of land that had been a little higher than the surrounding marshes; going through the village, farmers could admire or criticize the ricks of others. Farmers are generally very sensitive to the opinions of their peers; they also know that pride in appearance usually goes along with care to do a job well.

Once we had gathered up all the loose hay, using our peaks and the rake, the next job was to cut out the 'staddle'. The word is familiar today in the term 'staddle stones' – those mushroom-shaped stones once used to support corn stacks and barns to keep out rats and now sought after as expensive and fashionable garden ornaments. We used the word for the base layer of a rick: this was made up with old hay which had lost its goodness and would probably become spoiled anyway through its proximity to the damp earth. We first encircled the rick with the long wagon line, at about waist height, and tied the line tightly. We then made adjustments to the height of the line until it formed a straight horizontal guideline about three feet above the ground and right around the rick. Because of the downward lie of the hay it was much easier to tie the line high and cautiously to pull it down rather than upwards. With this line as a guide, uncle would cut away the base of the rick with a sloping cut. This was quite a tricky operation for the hay knife was heavy; that was not too much of a problem when it was used to cut vertically, but the inward-sloping cut required careful control and the strong wrists which are only developed over many years through milking cows by hand. For the sake of appearance the line had to be straight, like so many lines in farming, yet the knife must not cut the valuable wagon line. Like a ploughman's first furrow, the first cut had to be right. Once all the cutting was finished and the hay cleared away, any rain running down the sides would drop off at this level and fall outside the base of the rick. The cutting also gave a lively appearance to the rick; it no longer slumped on the earth, but seemed to grow out of the earth: which is precisely what it had done.

While normally we thatched all our ricks – as explained in the next chapter – I have to admit that we took a relatively easy way out with the great rick in the farmyard by roofing it with large sheets of corrugated iron. These had been acquired cheaply and fortuitously second-hand, so that although they were some of the few items that were not naturally occurring they had, in modern jargon, been 'recycled' and they could be used year after year and also had other temporary uses out of season. Their use certainly saved a deal of time when compared with the business of preparing reeds, making spars and stretchers and the labour of thatching itself; we were moving unthinkingly into the modern age of utility. (Eventually we had a permanent roof installed on iron columns, a so-called Dutch barn; 'Dutch' I suppose because it wasn't a proper barn, but only the top.) The head of the rick could be much less steep in this way and did not need to be made with as much skill.

The first operation was to handle a large ridge-piece of heavy timber, as long as the rick itself, up the ladders and place it along the centre line or ridge of the 'head' – the sloping top of the rick. Then the heavy sharp-edged sheets of iron, each about ten feet long and three feet wide, also

Rick Screw

had to be handled up the ladder; this was a clumsy and potentially dangerous operation. The iron sheets were nailed like large tiles by their short ends along the wooden ridge. The lower parts were secured by specially made iron fasteners or 'rick screws': shaped like very large corkscrews, these were skewered down into the hay through holes which had already been punched at intervals through the iron sheets. It was important that the sheets were placed so that these small holes were on the tops of the corrugations and not in the valleys where the water would run through into the rick. Sometimes we forgot to check and securely nailed a sheet to the ridge only to find when it came to putting in the rick screws that the sheet was the wrong way up and had to be laboriously 'un-nailed'. When all was well a second line of sheets was manoeuvred to 'under-lap' the top line.

Was this corrugated iron ugly? Although the absence of steep picturesque thatch may have been a visual loss, the waterproof qualities of the iron meant that the roof of the rick needed very little slope and so, like the more elegant lead roof of a Palladian building, it could scarcely be seen from the ground.

I said that the sheets had other uses and one of these illustrates how play and work, work and play, formed a continuum on the farm. When we were children we made our own slides using these iron sheets. My cousin and I would drag them to some place where they could be propped up at an angle, maybe against a branch of an apple tree or an old wagon or preferably against a large heap of discarded hay; anywhere so long as we could climb to the top. A modern safety officer, or maybe modern parent too, would have been quite horrified; we were after all only six and nine years old. The iron sheets were heavy and had sharp edges; if one was dropped or fell down it could cause a very serious injury if any flesh was in its way. In addition, where the holes had been punched for the rick screws, there were short jagged edges standing up which would severely gash our thighs or wrists as we slid down. We always therefore inspected the sheets carefully and made sure they were right side up, but occasionally after we had laboriously set up a slide we would realize that for some odd reason one or more holes had been punched the wrong way. After some consultation we might decide to use the sheet anyway, but just be careful to avoid the dangerous bit. Since there was no level part to slow us down at the bottom of these slides we just painfully hit the ground at full speed; a big bundle of hay solved that problem.

We learned to adjust the steepness: a slow, long, controlled slide or a steep fast one with a hard landing; steeper and steeper for excitement until we were almost falling down. We had a wonderful freedom to climb on or use almost everything on the farm, mostly unsupervised. In these ways we learned to be observant, to be agile, to calculate risks, to use judgement and to improvise. It was very different from the sterile fixed playgrounds of today; it was an excellent training for farming and for life.

❦4 Self-sufficiency ❧

As well as the large main rick which was made up of hay from several fields and served the cattle that were overwintered under cover in the farmyard, we built smaller ricks in more distant individual fields to feed stock that were kept out during the winter. Daily and seasonal farm work was much influenced by the fragmented pattern of land ownership in the area which was and is unusual in England, and possibly unique. As explained earlier, the history of the land had been a complicated mixture of settlements of various types – communal and individual – and of different periods, with a free-for-all in the seasonally flooded summer grazing areas.[8] Gradually these grazing areas had become regulated for shared use, then as common lands in some cases, and eventually were enclosed under individual ownerships. Most of the land historically had been in the direct ownership of the Crown or of the Church and although there was a manorial system the owners of the manors had their interests and residences elsewhere. The dissolution of the monasteries

and abbeys in the sixteenth century affected this
area more than many others since the Bishopric
of Wells and the Abbey of Glastonbury had been
the traditional large landowners for centuries;
there followed a long period of confusion and
disputes, but by the sixteenth century a number
of seemingly unrelated enclosed plots had already
been established. When the outlying grazing lands
were systematically enclosed in the eighteenth
century some persons suffered penury as in
most enclosures; but on the other hand 'one only
master' did not 'grasp the whole domain'. Possibly
because of the traditional flexibility of ownership
and use of the land there does not seem to have
been an emergence of powerful dominant families
who controlled, and sometimes even re-located,
whole villages as happened elsewhere in southern
England. The 'Squire' and the 'Big House' were
just fairytale elements to us as children, no more
real than the ruler of some petty German duchy
in a story by the Grimm brothers. Nor was there
the usual rigid English hierarchy of landowner,
tenant farmer (or yeoman) and farm labourer.
Flexibility in the system of land ownership
allowed a pluralistic society to exist in this
part of Somerset. Most people think of a farm,
correctly, as a discrete area of land encircled by a

Sale Poster of J.H.Palmer & Sons

Reproduced courtesy of Greenslade Taylor Hunt.

'From time to time, as farmers died or retired, these individual fields might come onto the open market.'

boundary of ownership: the so-called 'ring fence' type of farm. Many would-be entrants to farming find it impossible to get together the capital to purchase such a complete unit, and those who do may then be weighed down by large interest payments which distort both their enterprise and the farming environment. But here farmers could own or rent separate fields or groups of grounds which were often several miles apart and separated by the land of other farmers. From time to time, as some farmers retired or owners died, these individual fields might come onto the open market – although they could be sold privately of course – and were within the reach of keen and thrifty beginners. One small farmer started out as a labourer with one cow; he took his cow on a halter each evening to graze the roadside grass verges which were much wider in those days. When the council road men mowed the verges he would wait a couple of days for the grass to turn and then collect it as hay. His next stage was to rent a single small field and buy another cow. He went on to become a successful small farmer and for a time rented one of my fields.

In this way the mosaic of ownership was continually but slowly changing, although some fields of course, especially the 'home grounds' adjacent to a farmhouse, remained in the same families for generations. Another way into farming was through the purchase of grazing rights at the annual 'grass sales'. These were competitive auction sales at which a farmer could bid for the right to graze his animals for one season and possibly to make hay, subject to conditions of good management of the grass.

There was thus a true 'farming ladder' from the man or woman with one cow to the small number of larger farmers at the top with a few hundred acres. These larger farmers usually took an active part in the parish and maybe in local government affairs or on the Drainage Board; some might own a minor racehorse or ride with the hunt and maybe mix with the 'county set' but they were not strictly gentry and their influence was largely through the parish council which was elected democratically and for which anyone could stand. They in no sense had the arbitrary powers of a squire over people's lives and had to earn respect, which generally they did. The system on the whole produced people who were independent, energetic, individualistic, thrifty and enterprising – and covetous of grass and grassland: in some ways it resembled French peasant society as described by writers such as Balzac or Mauriac. If the farmers were sometimes hard men, they were no more so than farmers everywhere.

Clearly this pattern of ownership involved frequent movement of people and machinery and of farm animals along public roads. Fortunately the roads were not very busy then and speeds were slow. In addition, along with the enclosures, a network of green lanes had been developed and these provided access to many fields and, incidentally, very pleasant walks. In some cases, however, the only access was a customary route across fields which belonged to other farmers and this situation sometimes caused resentment although the routes had to be used to maintain the right of access.

Building small ricks in individual fields reduced the need for haulage to feed the animals kept out in the fields over the winter. These animals were temporarily unproductive stock – 'young things', yearlings, 'followers', in-calf heifers or 'dry' cows. A farmer had only to cycle or walk one or two miles, cut and feed some hay and return home, although he had to do this seven days a week. These field ricks were smaller and were not finished as tidily as the main ricks in the farmyard, but they still had to be made weatherproof and in particular they needed to be fenced securely against any cattle that might be in the fields.

Thatching of ricks was so important that even on larger corn farms which were able to employ several workmen the farmer would often carry out this skilled yet laborious operation himself; maybe it was also a symbolic expression of ownership and of the consummation of the harvest. On one-family farms of course the farmer did this job anyway. Today a large blue sheet of polythene, flapping in the breeze, suffices, but in the past the traditional materials were all available free from nature and would have been familiar to a mediaeval or even Anglo-Saxon peasant.

This link with an Anglo-Saxon past is not too fanciful; just behind the house in which I was born was a field which had been known for many years as 'Lady's Grounds'. Records show that the land in this area was once owned by a Lady Edith who became the queen of the last Saxon king, Edward the Confessor, in the mid-eleventh century, and who later granted ownership of the land to the Church. This is an intriguing item of local history, but I found it equally interesting to imagine the farmers or peasants who had used those grounds in the past: family after family, for generations, for centuries, for at least a thousand years; who had waited for the grass to grow each spring and

'The Hay Stack' by Henry Fox-Talbot, c.1840

Reproduced courtesy of the National Museum of Science and Industry.

'We did this in exactly the same way and Fox-Talbot's picture shows it very well.'

who fed their animals there and made their hay
and I liked to wonder how far back our skills and
knowledge really extended. I feel sure that those
people would have fitted easily into our ways of
working. Certainly, over a century before, in 1840,
Fox-Talbot the inventor of photography took a
picture of a hayrick (sometimes called 'The Straw
Rick') which looks exactly like the ones we made.
On that point of confusion I sometimes wonder,
when looking at Monet's pictures carefully,
whether some of those so-called hayricks in his
series of paintings on the subject were in fact
straw or corn ricks.

'Shalder' was the main material used for
thatching. This was the local name for bundles of
the common reed, *Phragmites*, which was allowed
to grow freely in some stretches of the ditches
and rhines for this purpose. It was essentially
the same plant which still grows extensively in
the Norfolk marshes and which under the name
Norfolk Reed has long been valued highly for its
durability as thatch for houses; it too is part of
the grass family. In the autumn the long, hollow,
jointed, stems with their feathery fruits die off
and dry to an attractive vibrant buff colour and
are then ready for use. We gathered the shalder by
clambering around on the steep banks of a ditch

or wading around in the soft mud and water at the bottom and cutting the reeds with a sickle or 'reaphook'. I quickly learned that it was important not to stand in one spot for too long or I would become immobilised as my boots sank slowly into the sticky clay; it was impossible to pull my boots out without taking my feet out of them first for as I tried to pull one foot upwards the other was forced further into the mud. The suction of the clay was surprisingly powerful and a little scary and I could understand how it had taken the lives of so many men on the battle-grounds of Flanders. The secret was to try to keep moving.

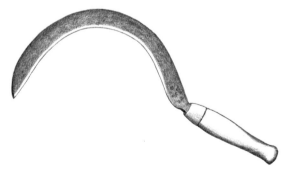

Reap Hook

It was fortunate that water levels were usually at their lowest in the autumn for these larger ditches were not just small roadside channels for diverting a little rainwater, but collectively were able to drain many millions of gallons of water from the moors. In England the term moors is generally used for wild upland areas, but the low lying Somerset Levels are also known as moors from the Old English word '*mor*' meaning a wild and marshy place. These Somerset Moors lie several feet above mean sea level, but since the Severn Estuary has the second highest tides in the world the land is well below the sea levels of the higher spring tides and is very vulnerable when these occur. Pumping stations have since been built to deal with this problem, but formerly in late winter when the annual flood waters came down from the hills and at times when the sea sluice gates or 'clyses 'in the sea walls at the outlets of the rivers had to be closed to keep out the sea, the river water was forced to back up into the drainage systems so that the ditches became filled to their brims and overflowed onto roads and into the lower rooms of some houses.[9] While many minor ditches had become silted up over time and were dry for much of the year, being of little use either as boundaries or for drainage, the larger ditches could swallow a car and drown the occupants. The reeds only grew where there was water all year round and, especially after the disastrous East Anglian floods of 1953 when the sea did break through, we were always deeply conscious of the close presence and power of the water as, cutting the shalder, we became swamp dwellers again for a while.

Willows provided the other two free items needed for the thatching: these were 'spars' and 'stretchers'. Most common was the white willow and its hybrids whose young branches were grown and harvested under a system known as 'pollarding'. Many people are familiar with the idea of coppicing in woodlands where trees or bushes, usually hazel, are cut at ground level and the young shoots are removed at intervals of several years according to the size of material needed. But where farm animals were present and would eat the young shoots, the trees were cut, or 'pollarded', at a height of about nine feet above the ground, out of reach of the animals. These attractive mopheaded trees used to be a characteristic feature of lowland meadows, but they have little place in modern farming and as they require regular cutting they have unfortunately become rather a nuisance and are being removed.

For spar-making, the young branches of pollard willows were cut when they were about one and a half inches in diameter; how the spars were made during the winter evenings is described in a later chapter. These spars resembled large double hairpins, about eighteen inches in length. Stretchers were long flexible willow twigs with all their side branches removed and were often prepared on site since they were most flexible when freshly cut. It was my job to prepare these stretchers and ensure a steady supply for my uncle as he did the thatching.

The 'head' or sloping part or 'roof' of a rick required careful construction. Essentially the head had to be steep, at least forty-five degrees, uniform and firm. If well-made in this way it could keep the bulk of the rick surprisingly dry even without any covering of thatch, but that was considered risky; any hollows or soft spots would direct the winter rains to the heart of the rick and the hay would rot. The thatcher required a long ladder that gave access to the whole area of work, ideally one long enough to lie at the angle of the head and yet reach the ridge at its top. Usually, if you were right-handed, thatching began in the lower right-hand corner of the head with the laying of a short row of shalder upright along the slope. A stretcher was then laid horizontally over the reeds and pegged in place at intervals with spars thrust into the firm hay, always at a slight upward angle for otherwise the spar would conduct water into the rick. You can see a single stretcher along the bottom of the thatch in Fox-Talbot's photograph, but the higher ones have been covered by the overlapping reeds. We didn't thatch as thickly and all our stretchers were exposed. The ends of the stretchers were continued over and down the ends of the rick a little way to bind the edge of the thatching tightly. Thatching continued across and up the rick. Since each layer of reed was laid over the one below, the work normally was finished off at the top, although some thatchers started at the top and slid the next row in under the first.

Thatching was best delayed for a month or

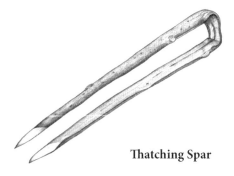

Thatching Spar

two after building to allow the hay to settle and firm up. This meant that ricks were exposed to the summer rains of August which strangely is one of the wettest months of each year. But if the thatching was carried out too soon the hay would later settle away from the spars, possibly tilting them downwards, and certainly leaving several inches of the spars exposed; the thatch would then no longer be held firmly and might be stripped away in a gale. There was always debate about whether the reeds should be laid with the thick ends, the butts, or the thin ends uppermost. Comparison was made with house-thatch where the butts were always laid downwards, but there, so it was argued, only the very ends of the butts were exposed to the rain. The thatch on ricks, on the other hand, was a relatively thin covering of reeds and most of their length lay open to the weather. Since all the leaves were left on the reeds to provide more bulk we always thought the water would flow better if the leaves were pointing downwards and that was how we did our thatching. It didn't look as tidy, but it worked well.

That was the rick protected from the weather;

now we had to protect it from the cattle themselves with a stout railing to keep the animals from gorging on the hay. Since we always built the ricks against a field boundary, the ditch or hedge provided one line of defence, or even two if the site was in a corner. Again, as for thatching, we found all the materials in the hedgerows and I don't remember a single fence post or rail ever being purchased. These fences had to be very strong, for the cattle would lean over with their long powerful necks outstretched, snorting, eyes bulging, muzzles twisting and striving towards the hay as they curled their strong tongues in anticipation – for cows do not bite their food, but mostly tear it off with their tongues – all the time straining their muscular chests against the rails. If they managed to get a taste of the hay this would encourage them to push even harder. Just two of those bodies would have been together capable of pulling a plough through the soil so sometimes they succeeded in breaking a rail and, on finding themselves in a sort of heaven, would quickly eat out an enormous cavern in the side of a rick. When after one or two tries, however, they still could not reach the hay, they seemed to accept defeat and give up. This meant that it was important to have the fence far enough from the rick so they could not get a first tempting taste. I don't know what the proper distance was exactly, but we knew that if we stood on the line of the railing, leaned our upper bodies forward at about thirty degrees, stretched out our right arm and could barely touch the rick it would be right. My uncle was a short, stocky, powerfully-built man – he would have been a good longbow-man in medieval times. His hands were toughened like leather from many years of outdoor work. I can still picture vividly that strong arm and hand outstretched as he went along the railing, checking, before the timbers were finally fastened down. This apparently simple action expressed both experience and confidence and, in particular, it seemed to symbolise that controlled human intervention between animals and their natural environment which is what farming is. But it was also a largely humane and balanced intervention, unlike the factory farming of today.

Working in the fields on a warm October day offered even more delights than were to be found in the farmyard. The grass, which during the hot summer had been cut and scorched and driven-over, had by now made a second growth, or flush, to create an even and luxurious green lawn: a 'lawn,' that is, in the eighteenth century sense of a large sward and not the pampered squares of suburban living. Technically this second sward is known as the aftermath, but to us it was always 'year grass,' I suppose because it came at the end of the year. In a good year this valuable growth could be grazed into the early winter, thus prolonging the grazing season, or even made into a second crop of hay. Around the rick meanwhile, the soft pillowy surface produced by accumulations of hay over the years had, by the germination of many thousands of hayseeds, been transformed into attractive bright-green mounds, like those of a Japanese garden. The leaves of the overgrown hawthorns which sheltered the rick from the north had become as colourful as any Japanese maple and the branches were heavy with deep-red haws, fruits of the creamy springtime froth of the May blossom. The still, clear, autumn air and the bright, low, penetrating sunshine gave to everything a detail and a depth which usually we see only in nature drawings and perhaps think them too perfect. But they are not. It is just that we look while the artist *sees*, and teaches us to see and to become aware of the intense 'being' of everything. Loose branches of dog-rose arched down from the large untidy hedge, displaying the brighter red hips; these the fruits of the simple and fragile five-petalled wild rose flowers of June.

    '…You know the way
    They nod and ask you not to pluck
    Them please, because they fade so soon.'

Climbing over and inter-weaving with everything were long chunky runners of brambles or blackberries, bearing an excess of fragrant and juicy bobbled fruits which were more tasty – and more healthy – than the contents of any sweetshop. A late brood of small brown and orange butterflies, the species known as 'Meadow Browns', fussed around the few remaining blackberry flowers. And just to remind us that *in arcadia ego*, the weak straggling creepers of woody nightshade proffered their glossy red and dangerous fruits. All this informal confusion was how a garden should be, not at all like the neat, stubby, formless plants often sold for convenience at modern garden centres.

Against this background of natural beauty we carried out our practical tasks. In summer, in preparation for making the new rick, most rails had been removed and some posts had been dug up and the holes they left loosely filled, for covered over with hay they would otherwise have been dangerous traps as we worked. Now these posts and rails which had been leaning against the hedge all through the summer were dragged out from the clutches of the fast growing brambles and grasses for inspection. Since they had been cut from free-growing hedgerow timber, they were, like the 'compass timbers' used in traditional shipbuilding, a variety of shapes and sizes. Each post had a short natural Y-shaped fork at the top, formed from the stubs of former stout branches. Depending on the species of tree from which it had been cut, one side of a fork might be longer and, crucially, more upright than the other; probably it had originally been the main stem. This stronger side would be put on the inside of the fence, closer to the rick, the better to contain the rail against the thrusting of the animals. But the main body of the post might be curved and the post could be set with this curve towards the rick – thus reducing the safe distance – or away, which was better. The fork and the curve might work together, or these effects might cancel each other out. Generally the advantage of the fork decided which way the post was set because the curved post could be set to lean outwards to overcome its disadvantage.

Nor were the rails straight, for they were cut from irregularly branching deciduous trees and generally carried several short lumpy branch stubs. Laid between two forked posts, this curvature meant that as a rail was rotated around its axis it moved noticeably nearer or further from the rick or became higher or lower and might settle more or less comfortably into the forks. Each arrangement was unique.

We laid each post therefore, as far as we could remember, beside its former post hole and the rails between, hoping to use last year's arrangement. But any timbers that were showing signs of rot or damage had to be discarded. Then we searched along those lovely hedges seeking for likely replacements. Usually this did not take long, for always, as we worked throughout the year, we had mentally noted any trees that seemed promising and often knew exactly where to look. We might even, while trimming the hedges some years previously, have removed the central stem in order to encourage that young tree to grow into a good fork. We picked up the metal-framed Swedish loggers' bow-saw, which was just a modern version of the old wooden frame-saws which had been tensioned by twisting a string, and within half an hour or less we had a new post or rail.

There is a special skill in digging a post hole economically and quickly by hand. Since the rails were of different lengths, the post holes were spaced accordingly and a new rail usually meant we had to dig a new post hole, and the old holes had to be located and dug out also. In that part of Somerset we were fortunate that there were no stones in the soil and so digging was comparatively easy, unlike in the brashy soil of the Cotswolds. What we called a spade was longer and narrower and heavier than a true garden spade and, although we always used them for gardening, they were really designed for digging ditches and narrow trenches for the laying of drains, sliding easily into the moist soft clay. The school master from Hertfordshire said that our 'spades' should properly be called 'clay grubs' but he took a rather superior attitude to everything we did anyway, seeing himself as part of the idealistic postwar movement to bring our country lives belatedly into the twentieth century.

When digging a hole for a post the aim is to remove as little soil as possible, which means keeping the hole small: sometimes maybe scarcely a foot square, for which our narrow, deep 'spades' were ideal. Anyone who is not used to this work will tend to make the hole progressively larger and larger at the top because he thinks it will be easier that way to shovel soil out of the hole, but he will end up moving three times the amount of earth and, very important, removing the surrounding firm soil which will be needed to support the post. But when you have chopped the sides a little deeper at the bottom of the hole, the skill is then to grip the spade low down and scrape the loose earth up and out with the spade held nearly vertically, but strongly, against one side. About a foot and a half of depth is sufficient, but this measure had to be adjusted according to the lengths of the posts to ensure the forks were at the correct heights; a certain amount of trial and error was involved inevitably.

Competitiveness seems to be natural to most members of the human race. I often think of that gentle Quaker character in *The Friendly Persuasion* who, even on the way to church with his family, could never resist the temptation to urge his horse a little faster when his neighbour's buggy was coming up behind. My uncle spotted that I was digging fast, trying to get ahead of him. He paused. 'Now, hang on a bit old boy,' he'd say. 'When two chaps are working together they always try to race. You go at it like that and you'll tire yourself, and then you'll have to rest. You must learn to pace yourself; learn to work at a steady pace where you can keep on going.' I recognised this as sincere advice, for he was not a fellow paid-hand suggesting we spin the job out a bit; he was paying my wages by the hour.

Ramming the soil firmly around the posts was the next and very important stage. Rammers could be bought, but usually they were too wide for our business, they had straight handles – and they cost money. Ours was simply a narrow, slightly tapered cylinder of wrought iron which had once been the bearing of an old wooden wagon wheel; this bearing had been hammered on to the thick end of a stout wooden handle cut from a willow tree. The handle had a slight curve and, although this may have appeared at first sight to be a crude defect, in use it meant that we could ram soil down in the small spaces around the post without skinning our knuckles on the rough posts and their forks; so we rammed with a slightly curving motion, like the darting tongue of a bee entering a flower.

There is a skill, too, in ramming. It's very important to add the soil little by little, especially at first, and above all to ram the first few inches at the bottom of the hole absolutely firmly all round before adding back more soil. If this bottom part is not tight then no amount of ramming later, when the hole is half full, will make the post firm.

You must also be aware not to ram one side too much or you will find the post has moved out of line, or is leaning. I know a landscape contractor who always fills his post holes with concrete. Apart from the unnecessary expense it is very difficult to remove large lumps of concrete when the posts eventually have to be replaced, as they will. There is a tradition in the country of taking a long view and considering what problems you are leaving for the next man, for the next man might be you in twenty years time. If our posts could not be pushed over by the efforts of several cows, then they surely would have been strong enough for a garden fence.

When the arrangement was to our satisfaction we fastened the rails to the posts with straps of iron which had been salvaged from the 'bonds' of old wooden barrels. These barrels were common then, for the area was famous for its farm-made cider; they are in fact still frequently seen, but now sawn in half and varnished, or painted black with white bands, as plant containers in gardens. Much more regrettable is the loss of the many ancient orchards that supplied the cider makers, and which alternated picturesquely with farmhouses and cottages along the village street and have mostly been built over with small bungalow estates and new houses. Recycled, too, were the nails we used, drawn from scrap timber or from some modified structure and which we later hammered straight in spare moments. We had a large and rusty 'nail tin' which once had been a beautiful upright, red tin with an oval glass window and had contained a well-known brand of cough sweet. Its capacity was about four pints, which seems to represent an awful lot of cough sweets. Every used nail and staple went into that tin and not necessarily for reuse, but because uncle always impressed on me the danger of a valuable cow getting a nail in her foot. If anyone dropped a nail we searched for it carefully until it was found.

We gathered up our tools and allowed ourselves some satisfaction for what we had done. The rick was firm, thatched and fenced; it looked good to us. Here and there, in confirmation, we gripped a sample rail or post and tried strongly to wobble it, not because we thought it might be weak, but because we knew it was not.

We divided the tools between us for carrying back to the car parked on the grass verge beside the field gate. The remains of a coil of vicious barbed wire, very heavy; a thick iron bar, used to break up hard soil or to lever almost anything, also heavy; the rammer, claw hammer, tin of nails, a slasher for clearing brambles, a small axe or hatchet for trimming timber, a spade each and the saw. Carrying some items in one hand and with a bundle of bars and handles on the other shoulder – you can pick them up, but can you carry them half-way across the field? – we set off. Soon the pain sets in to the trapezius muscle; you shrug your shoulder, trying to redistribute the weight a little; you hunch it up to thicken the muscle, all the time experiencing incipient tennis elbow in the other arm, bending that arm a little to reduce the painful stretching, walking more quickly to reach the gate sooner where at last, with relief, the whole lot can be flung to the ground. Then on to the cracked, brown leather of the back seat of the old pre-war Austin which was used for carrying many things, from taking very young calves to market to the occasional wedding.

When we were children we greatly enjoyed using those rustic fences as gymnastic balancing rails. Sometimes, even, a playful adult would join in, hoping to display his superiority (it was always a he) or perhaps to relive his recently lost childhood for a little time. All this took place

with the natural good-humoured banter and
competitiveness of play. Our challenge was to
try to walk along those rails and our goal was to
get all the way round, although the great variety
of rails meant that, as far as I can remember, no
one ever did. We had to be content with our own
personal best of two, three, four or more 'rails'.
Each time we fell off we took it in turns to 'go
round' again, ever hopeful of improving our
performance. The rails might be narrow or wide,
round or flattish, springy or steady and some
were very lumpy with old branch stubs which we
had to step over. At the posts we had to negotiate
our way between the forks and up or down to the
next rail. These obstacles meant of course that
we could not always be looking straight ahead to
help maintain our balance. Much more than the
plain and predictable play equipment of today,
this variety of hazards seriously exercised the
coordination of body and brain, which is said to
be so necessary for developing, and maintaining,
mental function – as the Chinese know well from
their Tai-chi exercises carried on into old age.

There was, too, another and more serious
hazard. Some cattle have a trick of getting down
on their front knees and reaching underneath
a barrier, so a line of barbed wire was usually

fastened in the space under the rails. As we climbed on to the fence and fell or jumped off we were dangerously close to that line of sharp metal spikes. Can you imagine a children's playground with barbed wire strung along the equipment? It didn't seem strange to anyone then. It truly was a different world.

For example, when I was about ten years old my grandfather one day gave me a large mysterious tin. Bonfire Night was near and, disappointingly, the shops had sold out of their small stock of fireworks. The tin was half-full of strange, small, black, shiny crystals which I didn't recognize. 'Now you can make your own fireworks,' he said. The crystals were gunpowder. Quite unsupervised I devised cardboard tubes bound with string and stopped up with clay, and fuses of cord soaked in paraffin. For the next few days I went around the garden and farm, setting off small experimental explosions and showers of golden sparks, but of course no harm was done.

❦5 Winter ❧

Winter, like old age, always comes as a surprise. Sometimes it comes slowly as pleasant autumn days seem to merge into one another while imperceptibly changing until, one morning, some line has been crossed and we see winter for what it is. Occasionally winter comes suddenly and dramatically when severe cold weather sets in as early as November. Why are we not prepared? There appears to be an optimism in human nature which makes us think that a fine summer will go on for ever, but in winter we confidently expect the spring.

A livestock farmer must be prepared for winter; this is the 'hungry gap' in the farming year. But how long is this gap? It will vary from year to year and from region to region: it even varies from farm to farm and from field to field, for a south-sloping field will receive more sunshine and its grass will grow sooner in the spring, and drier soils will warm up more quickly. Such differences did not concern us very much for all the land was flat and the soil was a uniform moisture-retaining clay. But slight differences in levels were very important. The average height of our village above mean sea-level was about seventeen feet; in my cousin's village three miles away it was nineteen feet; a difference of two feet in three miles, which is about as flat as you can find anywhere. But, as explained earlier, the land on which the settlements were located was slightly higher than that of the surrounding moors. On the moors, between the villages, the level might be only eleven, ten or even nine feet above the average sea. This small interval of seven or eight feet made all the difference between a field which flooded in winter and one which did not; indeed a difference of one foot could be significant since water always finds its level. On the moors, cattle had sometimes been marooned on temporary islands which happened to be a little higher than the surrounding land. These unfortunate animals, exposed to all weathers, were fed throughout the winter with hay brought to them by their owners on small boats.

It seems likely, but may be impossible to show, that those primitive boats were descendants of the dugout punts of the prehistoric lake-villagers. Although no longer made from a single tree, the bottoms of the boats were made from one large plank of elm whose dimensions determined every

other measurement by a system of rule-of-thumb
proportions. Some writers consider this to be the
most ancient boat design in Britain. Following the
major drainage schemes of the 1940s, however,
the extent of seasonal flooding was much reduced
and cattle were no longer fed from boats.

Each of the small farms spaced along the
village street had at its rear a field, or maybe two,
known as the home fields or 'home grounds'. The
arrangement was rather like that of burgage plots
along the main streets of medieval towns, but
on a larger scale and more dispersed. Generally
these home grounds were the oldest units of land
ownership and had been enclosed centuries ago
while most of the land had remained unenclosed
and shared as common grazing. The farm and
home field were an ancient unit as described for
example in a sale poster of 1878: *A convenient
MESSUAGE or FARMHOUSE, with the
Outbuildings, Barton, Garden, Orchards, and Home
Field thereto adjoining and belonging....* A messuage
is the collective name for a farm with its buildings
and land. Barton has several meanings, but one
meaning is simply 'farmyard' from an Old English
word *baretun;* it was commonly used in this sense
in the district. It was on these slightly higher and
more sheltered home grounds that the milking-

cows would spend most of the short winter days, close to the stalls where they could be 'brought in', milked and bedded down for the long nights.

By the beginning of the twentieth century all the outlying land had long been enclosed, but one local custom – blackberrying – seemed to reflect that older pattern of common land use. Because of the chore of milking cows twice a day, every day of the year, 'dairy country' was traditionally always more untidy than arable and sheep country where, between the peak activities of seed time and harvest, men could be kept busy on maintenance jobs such as laying and trimming hedges. In comparison many of our hedges were unkempt and consisted of full-grown hawthorn bushes or small trees with, growing among and through them, dense thickets of brambles or wild blackberry bushes which each autumn carried shiny, knobbly, juicy berries in abundance. As explained in a later chapter, these blackberries were avidly picked in large quantities each autumn for they could in those days be sold on commercially. Despite this monetary value however – and an element of keen competition associated with it – it was accepted custom that anyone could pick in anyone else's fields. It was as though the blackberries were still in common ownership and with this went an unwritten right of access to what was now private land – except, that is, in the ancient home grounds.

Cows 'in milk', that is still producing milk, or 'in-calf' and soon to produce might be brought in any time between November and the end of December depending on the weather and on how much grass was left in the fields. It is reckoned that grass keeps growing if the average temperature is above 40 degrees Fahrenheit. A map of isotherms shows that much of the south-western peninsula of England fulfils this condition in an average year, but we were right on the boundary and not every year is average. Even so, grass grows very slowly at these low temperatures and it doesn't provide the rich grazing necessary for producing milk. It is no accident that in temperate climates grazing animals in the wild naturally produce their young in the early spring, despite the stress of carrying their young throughout the hungry winters. Also, in cold or wet weather, milking in the comparative cosiness of the cowshed rather than in the open grounds was a much more pleasant job for the farmer and his helpers.

By early afternoon, presumably anticipating tasty food, shelter and the pleasure of being milked, the cows would gather themselves by the field gate.[10] Anyone who had a little spare time – my grandfather or grandmother, I or my cousin just home from school – with outstretched arms and maybe a stick held horizontally (children always like to have a stick), would enjoy helping my uncle and aunt to guide the cows into the shed. There was normally no shouting or arm-waving or hurrying or beating as you see on some farms and if we had done those things we would quickly have been told to stop doing them. It is well-known that cows let down their milk more easily and completely if they are calm and contented and a good cowman sees to this. The animals plodded in at their own pace and the job only took ten minutes.

So why were we needed? The cows would probably have walked in just as calmly on their own, and often did so. But my uncle, at least where his valued cows were concerned, was always thinking about how best to avoid trouble. Some little dispute among the cows themselves, maybe about order of precedence on going through the cowshed door – for cows have a sort of 'pecking order' – or a newly bought cow unused to the procedure, could lead to one running off over the dung-heap or into the orchard and perhaps injuring herself. Most cows are gentle, placid animals if handled well, but they easily become confused ('mazed' in local dialect) or panic ('go billied') and being herd animals this panic is infectious. The sort of loss that can take place is shown by the following incident. My uncle sometimes fed chopped apples to his cows and I remember one cow who, although not at milking time, perhaps fancied some more of the apples that were lying in the long grass in the orchard and tried to jump a barbed wire fence. She only managed to get her front legs over and we found her with her udder badly torn. Despite many weeks of treatment with the healing qualities of goose-fat, which was carefully saved every year from the Christmas goose just for such purposes, she never was any good again; I think most farmers would have sent her for slaughter straightaway, but my uncle thought he might heal her. On another occasion he had bought a new cow which was to be delivered by a cattle lorry from the market and he particularly asked if I could come along to assist when she arrived. Market-men handle strange animals in transit every day and do not usually treat them gently. When, after a long stressful journey, the steep ramp at the back of the lorry is let down and the folding gates opened out, the confused cow, let's call her Daisy, faces this scary slope – and cows, unlike goats or sheep, are not particularly nimble-footed; Daisy needs some persuasion to descend; and the driver is in a hurry.

Having rushed down the ramp, scrabbling desperately not to lose her footing, poor Daisy is presented with completely unfamiliar surroundings and the absence of her old herd of companions. This is when panic can set in. Daisy will need gentle coaxing, maybe with a handful of 'cow-cake' to persuade her to enter the strange cowshed. We don't want this to be an unpleasant experience for she will remember it and be troublesome in future. On this occasion the cattle lorry, unusually, was two hours late. We had waited around, chatting, for there was always plenty to talk about. We sat down, stood up, walked around for a bit. My uncle smoked several cigarettes. My grandmother brought out two cups of tea. Eventually the lorry arrived and Daisy was literally 'in-stalled' in five minutes. My uncle said, 'That's well done,' and taking some cash out of his pocket paid me for two hour's work. I protested that the job had only taken five minutes. 'That's not the point,' he said. 'That's a valuable beast and if anything happened to her it would be a big loss. I needed you to be here for those five minutes, but you've been here for two hours. You take your money, old boy, and welcome.'

Each animal knew its own stall. Walking impatiently in line along the narrow concrete walkway at the rear of the building, their hooves clopping and sometimes slipping a little as they stepped carefully across the several gutters that drained to the outside, each turned off smartly, like soldiers on parade, when opposite her own place. Any who made a mistake would quickly be butted or 'hoked' out by the rightful occupant following. To avoid disputes Daisy would already be haltered in her new place; soon the stall would be familiar to her too.

Such an arrangement is unusual today when cows spend their time in communal yards or covered sheds and are brought in turn to be milked in a hygienic 'milking parlour'. The old cowshed was set out like a traditional country house stables. Pairs of stalls were separated by stout wooden partitions; each cow was tethered to a large iron ring which was free to slide on a stout vertical post so that she could stand up or lie down as she chose, as a boat on a mooring post goes up and down with the tide. At the front of each stall – unlike in a stable – was a low manger for feeding, and in front of all was a low barrier; beyond this barrier was a corridor which provided access to the fronts of the stalls. This corridor was known as the 'fore-stall' and its principal function was the temporary storage of hay, ready for feeding. The dried grass which had been gathered and protected so laboriously was about to fulfil its destiny – the humble grass which supported everything.

I sometimes think that there should be a religion somewhere which worships the grass specifically. Certainly the Aztecs gave religious significance to the maize plant which had its own god, Cinteotl, but maize is a cereal. The Greek goddess, Ceres, as her name now suggests, was also goddess of the grain harvest and of much else besides. The truth is that animal products, meat and milk, were largely unattainable luxuries for most settled people throughout history and bread was far more important to them. Perhaps some nomadic pastoralists somewhere have such a god or goddess for the grass.

The layout of the farmyard was straightforward

and very pleasant. The cowshed was a long, low building, running east to west, and open on the south so that low winter sun shone right into the stalls and mild southerly winds kept them fresh; this aspect could be protected by large shutters when the weather was bad. Along the north side of the building, which was completely enclosed, ran the fore-stall passage which could be entered at either end. On the north-east corner stood the great hayrick, towering over all and sheltering the main entrance at the east end against cold northerly winds. Hay for feeding was cut out of the south-facing end of the rick, which made for a pleasant and warm aspect for the work, especially on sunny days. Beyond the rick was the old orchard. The cows came directly from the field gate and into the cowshed and did not stand around in the yard. Because of this arrangement the yard was never mucky or smelly as modern farmyards are; and its dry stony surface, lightly drifted with hay, merged into the grass of the orchard. Of course there had to be a dung-heap and this was conveniently situated to the south of the shed.

On the western end of the cowshed and separated from it by a short passage to the fore-stall was a loose-box: a square room where an injured cow, or a cow which was to calve soon, or young calves could be kept more freely. During the war it had been used to house pigs – a 'pigsty' – for although officially all produce had to sold to the government it was usually possible to keep back a bit of pork to supplement wartime rations. I remember that when I was very young a pig once rushed out of the sty and straight between my short legs, so that I was slid onto its back and carried away to the dung heap where I fell off. My main emotion was intense indignation.

Some writers on farming recommend tethering cows with chain halters. My uncle disagreed strongly. Not only did he prefer rope halters

which could be cut easily in an emergency; he had
devised a sort of slip-knot to fasten the end of the
halter to the iron ring. This knot stayed firm as
the cow moved her head, but could be released in
an instant by tugging the free end. For, as he said,
supposing there was a fire, or a cow somehow
managed to get the halter tangled and was in
danger of choking. Always he thought about
every aspect of his cows' conditions. He tried to
explain the mysteries of this knot to me: 'Put the
second 'ooze [noose, I think] through the first
'ooze and then the third 'ooze through the second
'ooze.' I never quite got the hang of it then, but
I think now it must have been the highwayman's
knot, used by highwaymen, and by cowboys, to
tether their horses ready for a quick getaway
and sometimes by sailors to tie a small boat to a
difficult-to-reach fixture.

Timbers of all shapes and sizes had been used
when the cowshed was constructed, many years
ago: round or square, straight or crooked, and
often waney-edged – that is where the rough
surface of the tree has been left along one edge
of the timber. Each stall showed variations in
construction where the carpenter had modified
his general design according to the timber
which he had at hand, as in the interiors of old

windmills or watermills. I find this delightful for you can imagine the working of the craftsman's mind as he overcame each problem; *you see the craftsman's struggle* and this awareness is a form of communication across time which perfection does not always provide.

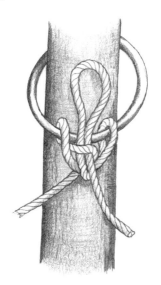

Herdsman's knot

Although at first sight each stall appeared similar to the rest, organic variations in detail and texture meant that we could recognize each one individually. The construction thus displayed the admirable aesthetic characteristic of 'variety within uniformity'. This simply means that there is potential for an observer to enjoy interesting detail within an overall satisfying basic form; it is one of the the secrets of the attractiveness and interest both of natural forms, such as trees, and of traditional buildings, whatever their style. A modern cowshed – or any building – of smooth concrete and tubular steel does not stimulate the imagination nor allow such intimate identification with place and time. I don't know whether the cows were aware of these differences, but if they were not then presumably they must have been able to count to find their stalls as they did: 'Yours is the tenth one down on the right dear'.

During the summer the stalls had been brushed out, hosed down and painted with whitewash or lime-wash – the traditional country decorating material, cheap and hygienic both for houses and for outbuildings. Everything was now in place for the winter: the cows were contentedly crunching hay, snorting and breathing heavily as they do and rattling the halter rings as they tossed their heads to keep the hay in their mouths, or lowered their muzzles to seize more hay. In the fore-stall, in ancient tins and bottles, were traditional medicines such as Stockholm tar for coughs or goose fat for sore teats; dusty hessian sacks of concentrated feeds; storm lanterns and matches – highly dangerous if used carelessly; and curry combs, brushes and a hand operated clipping machine for grooming the animals' coats to keep them – and their milk – as clean as possible.

Outside in the farmyard and conveniently close to the door which led into the end of the forestall was the great hayrick. I don't remember its exact dimensions, but it would have been about 25 feet long, 20 feet wide and maybe 15 feet high on average which with a density of what a valuer would call, inversely, 'ten yards to the ton' (cubic yards that is) would have contained about 31 tons of hay. A variety of foodstuffs in many combinations can be used to make up rations for cows, but uncle kept them very simple, using mostly hay and bought-in concentrates such as 'cow-cake' with plenty of water to make up for the lack of succulent foods. He had never enjoyed arable farming and once the war was over put down all his grounds back to grass as soon as he could and he didn't feed mangolds or kale (which are 80 or 90 per cent water anyway) as some did. Allowing therefore for a rather bigger ration of hay than usual I calculate that the one rick alone could feed 25 cows for 105 days or about three and a half months. With luck this would

see him through until April and the spring when
the grass would start to grow again; if not there
was another rick in the adjacent home ground.
Our little self-contained world was set up for the
winter and that great pile of dried grass was its
principal energy source.

Fox-Talbot's pioneering photograph, variously
titled 'The Straw Stack' or 'The Hay Stack', shows
how hay (straw is usually considered to be the
dried stalks of cereals) was being cut out from the
rick for feeding to animals more than 170 years
ago, and very probably for hundreds of years
before that. We did this in exactly the same way
and Fox-Talbot's picture shows it very well.

A start was made by placing an old wooden
ladder up to the corner of the rick. When thinking
about ladders the terms 'old' and 'wooden' are
so significant that such thoughts justify a small
digression since ladders were used almost daily in
our various tasks. There was a man in the village
who made ladders. He selected the straight,
narrow 'bole' or trunk of some young coniferous
tree – larch timber would have been ideal because
of its resistance to rotting, but I'm not sure he
always used larch. He planed off the bark and
branch stubs and cut the pole right down the
middle symmetrically, which required some skill.

The rungs he must have turned up on some old lathe, possibly even a pole-lathe worked by a treadle like those used by the Chilterns 'bodgers', which I have discovered are surprisingly efficient, although hard on your hips. It is a very simple device: a rope is tied to a springy branch of a tree overhead; the rope is wound around the piece of wood to be turned and then down to a foot treadle. Depressing the treadle revolves the wood for the cutting stroke and the springy branch raises the treadle ready for the next stroke. It seems very primitive so I once asked a bodger how many revolutions his lathe made in a minute and he replied that he had never counted. So we did count: 500 revolutions per minute, which is as fast as the low speed that I often use on my electric lathe. At this speed a bodger could make many dozens of Windsor chair legs in a day, which was just as well as the rate of pay per dozen was pitifully low.

The rungs were thicker in the middle which is where the maximum strength is needed, as 'beam theory' tells us, and which also made an attractive and functional shape. To fix the ends of the rungs into the sides of the ladder, the ladder maker bored a series of holes along the centre of the cut pole, which again according to beam theory is in the neutral plane and so does not affect strength very much. He probably used a traditional one inch centre-bit (a 'wunner' as the old chair-makers called it) which any blacksmith could make with its simple design, and a hand-brace. In fact the whole operation was similar to the making of plain Windsor chairs, and I don't suppose the ladder maker had ever heard of beam theory.

In principle the use of the 'grown' timber for the sides of the ladder was good, giving natural strength, whereas 'sawn' timber from a larger log could have a dangerous weakness if the grain of the wood was 'short': that is, if the fibres of the wood did not run parallel for the whole length. But the possible defect of the round timber was a 'dead' knot. Young trees are 'brashed' by foresters: that is, dead lower branches are knocked or cut off, for if this is not done the tree will grow around these dead parts and they will become weak points in the timber.

It should have been quite easy to check for the presence of dead knots before buying a ladder – except that the ladder maker always coated his ladders thickly with 'Air Force blue' paint whose exact source was, incidentally, also murky. 'Never trust a painted ladder, nor a painted "ooman" [woman]' an old house painter told me and I have always considered it good advice; nor, it may be added, a freshly painted boat if it is made of wood. We had several ladders of various lengths since they were not adjustable. One, a short one luckily, after a few years developed a crack on one side and as the paint wore away we saw the cause was a dead knot; many years ago one branch in the forest had been missed or not cut off cleanly and now this small omission endangered our safety. Of course the ladder maker ought to have rejected that piece. We always made sure the crack was uppermost in use and so closed up under stress, and we carried on.

The first operation in opening up a rick was to remove a square yard or so of the thatch which had been laboriously laid on just a few months earlier. In the case of the great rick it was one sheet of corrugated sheet-iron which had to be taken off. To provide a working position for this job the ladder must extend beyond the top of the rick. Given that the traditional spacing between rungs is about ten inches, the ladder on the corner of the rick in Fox-Talbot's photo can be estimated to be about thirteen feet long. Clearly, to work on the highest part of the rick, a ladder of maybe twenty-five feet would have been needed. Such a long ladder is very heavy and difficult to manoeuvre. The photo shows how the ladder is liable to slide off sideways along the slope. To counteract this tendency the ladder must be placed not quite at a right angle, but pointing slightly into the centre – but not too much or it would slide the other way. There is a feel to a firm ladder, which comes with experience; you grasp both sides and shake the ladder and usually any tendency to slip will be felt.

Then it was up the ladder with that heavy hay knife which had been used for trimming the rick in the autumn. The first cut was always the most difficult. A cube of hay (a 'tod') about two and a half feet square was cut out, but it was not possible to reach over to do this completely from the ladder; you had to kneel on the wobbly column of hay which became more wobbly as you cut deeper until discretion suggested that's enough; it was rather like sawing off the tree branch you were sitting on, which is generally considered to be not a clever thing to do. It was important while cutting to keep the handle of the knife firmly against the surface of the previous cut above – this was the purpose of the crank in the handle – otherwise the face of the rick would become cumulatively more and more concave and would attract ridicule from anyone who saw it. The aim was to produce a flat vertical face as shown in Fox-Talbot's photograph.

When the cutting was finished the knife was thrust firmly into the rick, for you didn't want that thing to fall and split your head open or slice off an arm. The handle can be seen in the photograph, quite high up and out of reach of small children who might, as we did when young, clamber up the ladder and on to the terraced hay. You then climbed gingerly back on to the ladder, went down a few steps and slid the first tod onto your shoulder, and climbed down, one hand on the hay and one sliding down the side of the ladder. Although cutting out the rick in this way seemed to be a straightforward job when it went well, I think it was one of the most tricky and potentially dangerous things we had to do and I sometimes wonder what a modern safety officer would make of it.

Based on an average density for hay, a tod of hay that size and, say, two feet high would weigh about 100 pounds; a foot and a half was more manageable. Its bulk meant that it was impossible to balance a tod just on your shoulder so it was carried either on the upper back as you stooped over like an old person or, more elegantly, it could be carried on the top of your head, as African women do so impressively with their burdens; the fore-stall door was extra high to allow for this although I, being tall, still had to make a little curtsey as I went through. One tod was sufficient for the maintenance ration of four or five cows each day. We usually filled the length of the fore-stall each time with maybe two days' rations. This made yet another feature in our young 'play': tumbling, jumping or even doing forward rolls over all the tods in succession until we arrived breathless and with our hair full of hayseeds at the end of the fore-stall – and then doing it all over again. But as we grew a little older and taller the magic somehow went out of some of those games; the fore-stall seemed less mysterious, the tods of hay smaller and the hayseeds curiously seemed more irritating. It seemed not to be such fun anymore and we didn't quite understand why: a development of feeling and awareness described so poignantly by Dylan Thomas in his wonderful poem *Fern Hill*.

There were compensating pleasures, however. Because dust from the hay would get into the milk, the cows were fed only their concentrates before milking, each rationed roughly according to the amount of milk she was producing. When all was finished and the milk had been taken away to the dairy, we went along the fore-stall giving each animal a few inches' thickness of hay. There is some deep atavistic satisfaction in being among these large animals when they are contentedly munching their hay in the yellow lamplight while there is darkness and cold outside. Perhaps it goes back to the days of the old longhouses when people lived with their animals; perhaps even earlier when cattle were gathered into pounds each evening for security. A few years later, after my Francophile French language teacher had persuaded me that I would be able to live off the hospitality of the French country-people, I was hiking in that beautiful country. He was right about the hospitality – it was not so very long after the war and I think they were used to hiding escaped RAF pilots – *'Ahh! C'est un petit anglais!'* I think the *petit* referred not to my size, for I was quite tall, but as a general term of endearment. I was often allowed to sleep in barns and such places, which suggests a large degree of trust towards a stranger. One night, after a simple meal of turnip soup and hard rye bread in a farm kitchen, I was shown a big pile of loose hay in a cowshed as my bed, among large red French cows. Unlike Caedmon, I was not visited by God in a dream, but I had one of the best night's sleep

I can remember and when I woke up I found I had sunk about three feet into the loose hay.

6. The Farmhouse

My grandparents' farmhouse was the control centre and crossroads of everything that happened on the farm and of much else besides. The farmhouse kitchen had that special and delightful character which only farm kitchens can have I think. It combined – or perhaps I should say that it contrasted – relaxation with a firm and constant purpose. Cosy domesticity merged with the hard reality of physical labour, and with a continuing awareness of implacable nature, and each caused the other to be felt more keenly. Here late breakfast was cooked up after morning milking, and often a rather late lunch when that suited the rhythm of the work. Here a quick, cosy, mug of tea was taken on dusky winter afternoons before we faced the rigours of afternoon milking, even perhaps as cold rain lashed against the darkening window panes. This was where in summer, after lunch, we each slumbered briefly in our chairs in a deep silence marked only by the resonant ticking of the large American clock which hung on the wall; but when the clock began to make the whirring sounds which presaged its striking two o'clock we roused ourselves to face again the work of making hay in the fierce afternoon sun. Here, too, important decisions were made about practical questions, such as when to bring the cows off the fields in autumn, when to turn them out to grass in the spring, which fields to close off for hay, which fields to mow first and when, and so on. All this involved careful analysis of the tendencies of the weather, not only for the day or the morrow, but for the long term also: would it be a hard winter, a late spring, a dry summer?[11] For this of course the only guidance in those days was old country weather lore. If the rooks nested high up in the elm trees in the spring there would be a fine summer; if the hawthorn berries were unusually plentiful in autumn there would be a hard winter and so on. These long term predictions were not always reliable, although swallows flying low were a good indication of rain in the next few hours.[12] Sometimes there were more secretive meetings, which were none of my business, about investment and purchases, and profit or loss.

In the evenings, in the soft yellow light of the paraffin lamps, we played drafts or table skittles, or my grandmother would read aloud to us all. I particularly remember Ruskin's *The King of the Golden River* which to me as a young child seemed especially magical. If the weather was cold enough for a fire, it was fun to make toast, using those long toasting forks (which are not mere antique ornaments) so that our fingers didn't burn, holding slices of bread in front of the fire bars which contained the glowing logs and being careful not to burn the bread by impatiently thrusting it too close; then adding golden, melting butter. It had to be the right sort of fire; a dark, smoky or newly lit fire would not make toast, and as there were no electric toasters we couldn't have toast just whenever we wanted; but I know we appreciated it more when we could.

Built sometime in the first half of the nineteenth century, of warm red brick, the house showed a little of that lingering influence which classical design had on simple domestic architecture for a time before the fussiness of the Arts and Crafts Movement began. The layout was symmetrical; an imposing six-panel front door opened into a dark entrance hall with one major room on each side. The kitchen was the room on the left. Each room was lit by a large white-painted sash window with slender glazing bars and low sills. On the upper level three more sash windows indicated the presence of three bedrooms. The appearance of the whole front was balanced and well-proportioned. It faced a small traditional 'knot' garden, a pattern of low, clipped, box hedges filled with cottage garden flowers such as sweet William, love in the mist, monkshood, grannie's bonnets and carnations, and flanked by lilacs and kerria hedges. Beyond this garden was a large bed of strawberries, then the extensive kitchen garden with areas of gooseberry and blackcurrant bushes and a whole bed of rhubarb. Growing in the hedge at the end of the garden were four large plum trees bearing sweet, purple plums in season where each afternoon when school had finished I searched eagerly for windfalls. In one corner of the garden a little wicket gate led into the orchard.

The façade was, however, the limit of any classical tendencies. There were no classical details of any sort on the house, such as decorative corner stones or quoins, and the steep roof was gabled and tiled with no suggestion of a parapet. Inside, there was a pleasant surprise in the kitchen:

a traditional inglenook fireplace, a sort of room within a room, and an old, black, cast iron cooking range with an integral oven and a couple of adjustable saw-toothed hooks for hanging kettles over the narrow fire. Although quaint and now quite obsolete this type of cooking range was the best available, for the up-market Aga had only recently been invented, in 1929, and that in Sweden. This was a typical nineteenth century farmhouse kitchen and not at all the neoclassical parlour which might have been expected from the outside. This cosy little room within a room contained two armchairs, one each side of the fireplace, and in the recesses formed by the protruding chimney breast were piles of books. Over the entrance to the inglenook was a very large beam, about twelve inches thick. On the front of the beam was fixed what looked like an object of modern art: a piece of twisted grey metal about three feet long. We children sometimes asked what it was; but this asking was just for the thrill of being told, as we might ask for a familiar story, for we already knew. It was part of an enemy bomber which had crashed nearby (of which, more later). This relic seemed to embody a kind of symbolism for my grandfather, something more than a mere curiosity, for it certainly wasn't pretty. I think, too, we found it difficult to believe, for aeroplanes were rather beautiful mysterious things which we saw up in the sky. It was not easy to equate them with this commonplace yet slightly sinister piece of earthly metal.

The house faced east, to the morning sun, which was appropriate for lives which required early rising every day. Thus the inglenook at the end of the room was on the south wall and was illuminated only by a small four-paned window, since people who spend most of their time out of doors do not generally seek large sunny windows. Everyone in the village thought it extremely odd when a newcomer couple from Birmingham had the first picture window ever seen installed in their cottage, especially as they did not draw their curtains at night.

To the right of the inglenook was an old door which opened onto the most un-classical stairs, narrow and winding right back on themselves, constructed of rough dark-brown wood, every step of which creaked in unison when any one part was stood upon, as though the whole structure was in danger of collapsing. The stairs led directly to the first bedroom, and as there was no handrail on the landing it was possible to get out of the wrong side of the bed and fall directly down the stairs. This arrangement was not uncommon in old houses and possibly it was the origin of the traditional saying, when someone is unusually bad tempered in the morning, that they 'must have got out of the wrong side of the bed'. It was necessary to pass through the first bedroom to get to the second, and so through the second to reach the third: an inconvenient arrangement, but one which I have seen in some very great houses. In the third room was a feature which was rather unusual for a bedroom. On the back wall of the room was a door which opened into space. It was rather like the doors in warehouses and barns which are used for taking in goods hoisted up to the second floor, and that may have been its function for no bedroom furniture could have been carried up those stairs. We were of course warned not to walk through that door, but it was never locked or bolted; indeed it had only a simple latch. As usual we were trusted to be sensible, but I always had a slightly uneasy dream-like feeling about that door which seemed to go nowhere.

No one speaks today of a kettle 'singing'. The electric kettle boils up noisily and then switches

Kettle Hanger

off. But if you don't have an electric kettle –
indeed, you don't have electricity at all – and
there is no hot water system, the only way to have
readily available hot water is to keep a kettle or
two permanently over the fire. This is the function
of the adjustable kettle hanger: the kettle can be
raised to a height where it is just 'off the boil'.
And then it sings, not throatily like an electric
kettle, but softly and harmoniously with a sort
of sighing, sizzling contented sound. In a typical
late afternoon scene in winter my grandfather is
sitting in the left-hand chair, reading a book by the
light of the small four-paned window, struggling
a little for the day is fading and he begins to
glance at the lamp, wondering whether to light
it. But it is wartime and paraffin is rationed and in
short supply. So he closes his book and turns his
head a little to gaze into the fire whose wood fuel
is rationed only by his labour. On his left knee is a
large white and black cat, stretching out to enjoy
the fire's warmth and purring deeply. From time
to time the cat, in its pleasure, inconsiderately curls
its claws into my grandfather's leg, but he doesn't
seem to notice. My cousin and I are sitting on
little stools in front of the fire, making our toast.
Behind us the clock ticks slowly, each emphatic
'tock' of its regular tick-tock sound invoking a

low sympathetic trembling of its gong. My uncle is sitting in his favourite Windsor chair by the kitchen table, also staring at the fire, and except for taking an occasional slow deliberate sip of his tea, he is quite motionless and composed; people who spend long hours in hard physical work every day do not fidget since for them it is simply a pleasure to be still. Very likely he is puzzling over some management problem of the farm. Or perhaps he is simply savouring the warmth and stillness just a little longer before rousing himself with his favourite expression, 'Well, my time's money,' to go outside again to his work. Seated in the right-hand chair by the fire my grandmother is darning socks, for darning was a never-ending task, especially for women, until nylon material was introduced into socks and pockets. And all the while the kettle sings its happy *continuo*.

In the eighteenth century there was a fashion for building neoclassical fronts onto seventeenth century or even medieval houses. The interior features of my grandparents' house resembled those of many smaller houses of the seventeenth century. Here then the builder, for surely there was no architect, working in the nineteenth century had combined the ideas of two previous centuries into one construction. Sometime early in the twentieth century the size of the house had been doubled by a very large lean-to extension built along the whole length of the back and whose roof reached right up to the roofline of the main house to produce what is sometimes called a 'cat-slide' roof. This extension was of course known as the 'backhouse' and its effect was to turn the whole house plan into something more like the neoclassical 'square house' except that the backhouse had no upstairs. Therefore one interior wall, the former outside wall of the old house, was two stories high, extending up into the gloomy roof space and there, high up in one dark corner, was the other side of the mysterious door.

Half of the area of the backhouse was used for storage of produce. Large bowls contained hams that were heaped up with salt in a process of preservation known as 'salting'. On a wooden table were stacks of *papier mâché* trays containing eggs waiting to be sold. There would be cans of the day's milk – dangerously unpasteurised – measured out for various parts of the extended family; possibly some freshly made cream cheese drying out and maybe some soft white mushrooms plucked early that morning from the dewy grass. In the autumn and winter there were large golden pumpkins which had flourished freely in the summer on the fertile dung-heaps in the fields. Often these pumpkins had letters etched in scar tissue where we had scratched our initials when they were very tiny and watched them magnify as they grew, each of us hoping that our pumpkin would become the largest which then would have the honour of being served for Christmas Dinner. There were green and white stripy marrows, sacks of earthy potatoes and turnips and many boxes of apples and of blackberries in the autumn. All this self-sufficient produce was the outcome of a great deal of hard work by various members of the family on top of all their normal work.

The other half of the backhouse was used as
a kitchen, especially in summer when there was
no fire lit in the old kitchen. It contained a large
shallow earthenware sink, a single cold-water tap,
a quite modern paraffin cooking stove and oven,
a 'cricket' table – that is, a round, scrubbed wood
table with three legs – and an old high backed
wooden settle which had been made especially
to fit into the house of my great grandmother
before the Great War and now, fortunately, is just
the right size for my own front porch. On the
table each morning were laid out the vegetables
and fruit which had been harvested from the large
kitchen garden, ready to be prepared for the day:
there might be peas to be 'podded' or beans to be
sliced, gooseberries or blackcurrants to be 'topped
and tailed', a cabbage, potatoes of course, sticks
of rhubarb, plums and so on. A very large brick-
built walk-in cupboard served as a cool larder
where meat, uncooked or cold, butter and cheese
were stored. My grandparents took food and its
preparation very seriously and the main meal
of the day was always substantial.[13] A special
feature which may seem quaint now, but was then
the most convenient and safest way of washing
clothes, was the 'copper'. This was a large, upside-
down dome-shaped metal container which was

built into a brick structure with a small fireplace underneath so that water, soap and clothes in the container could be boiled up together. The clothes were agitated with a special three-pronged stick called a washing dolly. Primitive as this may seem, it was a great advance on the dangerous business of boiling a bucket of water on a fire. I'm not sure why it was called a copper since the container was made of iron, but in big houses I think large copper cans were used for washing because the rust from iron may damage fine clothes. A similar 'copper' can be seen preserved in William Morris's old house at Kelmscott Manor where his daughter, May, lived a simple country life until she died in 1938.

On the subject of garden produce, I have one of the original *Dig for Victory* leaflets distributed in 1941 in which the then Minister of Agriculture and Fisheries exhorts gardeners to preserve their produce through the winter as the submarine war against our merchant ships intensified in the North Atlantic:

To everyone who has or can get an allotment or garden.

Owing to the shipping position we shall have need of every bit of food we can possibly grow at home.

Last summer many gardens had a surplus of perishable vegetables such as lettuce and cabbage. This winter those same gardens are getting short not only of keeping vegetables such as onions, carrots and other root crops, but also of fresh winter vegetables such as late cabbage, savoys and kale.

We must try to prevent that happening this year. Next winter is going to be a critical period.

This leaflet tells you how to crop your ground to the best advantage so as to get vegetables all year round.

Please study it carefully and carry out the advice it contains.

My grandfather put this advice into practice very conscientiously and continued to do so for many years after the end of the war. I too was expected to spend many hours digging the large garden, even when I was scarcely taller than the spade itself, although I was always paid a fair amount of pocket money for my work. The habit of 'digging for victory' was carried over into the austerity years after the war and most people had large vegetable gardens from which potatoes and other root crops for use throughout the winter were clamped – that is preserved by being packed in layers of straw and covered over with soil. Runner beans were salted away in stone jars; fruit was bottled in airtight 'Kilner' jars, and winter greens such as cabbage and Brussels sprouts grew in the garden throughout the cold months. Spare bedrooms were full of golden pumpkins and of boxes of apples – those varieties that were good 'keepers' – from which my grandmother daily made apple pies which I never tired of eating.

On the matter of the rationing of paraffin I have the Ministry of Fuel and Power's 'Priority Authorisation' for the supply of kerosene to my mother's house. For August 1943 it was just five gallons for the whole month, rising to eight gallons for October as winter approached: less than two gallons per week. You couldn't do much cooking or heating on that amount and my mother and I often stayed at the farm house where fuel and food could be shared.

My grandmother, born in 1886, was one of a family of ten children, but being female and not the oldest it seemed very unlikely that she would ever inherit my great-grandfather's farm. The last decades of the nineteenth century, however, were a difficult time for English farming. Robert Peel's controversial repeal of the Corn Laws, effective from 1849, were not at first detrimental to agriculture in England and the prosperous period known as 'High Farming' continued for a quarter of a century. Then the opening up of the American prairies and developments in transport led to cheap imports and a long agricultural depression. Five of my grandmother's siblings, like thousands of other English men and women, followed the money and emigrated to the United States of America where they settled in the prosperous industrial and prairie State of Illinois. There they applied their farming and business skills, made a great deal of money and I suppose could be said to have contributed in a small way to the decline of farming back home. They kept in touch through regular letter writing – I still have many of their letters – and I can just remember one of their sons, back in England as a very tall, clean looking American 'GI', visiting the farmhouse during the war and banging his head as he entered the unfamiliar low doorway of our old English kitchen.

The remaining brother, great-uncle Henry, was an excellent man with horses and moved away to make his career in the high class hunting and

horse riding communities of Gloucestershire. He
had a delightful old cottage in the valley of the
Severn, so pretty with its garden and with roses
and 'japonica' – a species of *Chaenomales* – around
the front porch that it was almost a cliché; like a
water colour by A. R. Quinton. Two more sisters
moved to other villages when they married. One
went 'down-country' to the beautiful Brendon
Hills and once a year, around Easter time, my
grandparents took my cousin and me to visit. We
caught a country bus from Taunton Castle and
then walked the last two miles along a narrow lane
bordered with high banks covered in pale yellow
primroses and startling white 'Star of Bethlehem'.
The farm was tucked into a south-facing hill and
surrounded by wild foxgloves and ferns and if we
were lucky we might spot some wild deer. It was
all quite different from the flat lands we knew, but
in fact not as idyllic as it seemed. My great aunt
had married a very hard man who did not treat his
cows or his only son well on that lonely farm; the
farm was approached by way of a farmyard deep
in mud and ordure and beside a large pond full of
green slime. No doubt it has all been gentrified
now.

These various departures left only my
grandmother in the village and one sister, great-

aunt Alice, who never married; the odds on my grandmother getting the farm had shortened considerably, especially when my great-grandfather followed his sons abroad, leaving my great-grandmother to run the farm. But this was all too late. My grandmother was not a person who just waited around for favourable events, but in 1907 good luck favoured her. Among my grandmother's papers is an old, itemised invoice, written in beautiful copperplate hand writing, of the building of a house in a nearby village in 1834. The details of prices and wages are of some interest in themselves – incidentally, the total cost of the house was £164 – but for my grandmother the significant event was that in 1882 the son of the builder married her mother's sister Eliza. Eliza seems to have had no children so that when she died as a widow in 1907, apart from some minor bequests – *'to my said Niece Polly my writing Desk and to my Niece Ellen my large Oak Table'*– her estate of £986-13s-3p was divided equally among the nephew and four nieces who had remained in England. Thus my grandmother, who had married in 1906, inherited a year later a sum of money which was sufficient in those days to buy a very desirable house. Then in 1911 the house which was to become the new farmhouse came on the market.

In the poster advertising the sale by auction the farmhouse is described as follows:

DWELLING HOUSE

Outbuildings, Good Garden, Orchard and Apples,

viz –

All that convenient Freehold Dwelling House, with Stable, Outbuildings, productive Garden and Orchard, numbered 492 and 494 on the Ordnance Map.

After the Sale of the Above Property the Apples &c in the Orchard will be Sold by Auction.

Apples were valuable because they were the raw material of the local cider trade. Some apples were stored for domestic use over the winter, but most were sold by the wagon load, quite literally. For a mile or so along its length the village street was lined by continuous orchards. Over the last half century most of these orchards have disappeared, but they are clearly shown on an old map of 1886 with houses and farms set among them. A common sight in autumn was large heaps of apples under the trees, awaiting collection. They were shovelled up with large wooden shovels, for in those days the quality of the fruit was not very important; probably quite a few worms and slugs ended up in the cider press and maggots certainly did.

My grandparent's orchard contained about twenty-five large apple trees; each tree was of a different variety and every tree was a challenge to be climbed, with various degrees of difficulty.[14] We ate large numbers of apples, both cooked and directly picked off the tree *ad lib*. The first apples to mature in the season were the yellow-green *Codlings*, good 'cookers' but not good 'keepers' so from late August onwards we had an almost daily diet of apple dumplings and apple pies. A delicious 'eater', that is a desert apple, which followed soon after was the *Morgan Sweet* with a yellow skin and creamy flesh. Another favourite eater was the *Tom Pud*, or *Tom Putt*, with a red and white stripy skin and crisp white flesh. It was said, and in my experience was certainly true, that you would never find a mature Tom Pud that didn't have a maggot in it. Always there was just one tiny pin-sized hole on the outside and somewhere in the flesh would be a tiny grub; it was so difficult to find that usually we just ate them without looking. Today the maggot would be deterred by a chemical spray and we would eat some of the chemical instead; I rather think it was safer to eat the maggot. It puzzled and intrigued us that this apple which was widely considered to be the most perfect eating apple should, uniquely, always contain this imperfection.

Other varieties included the dark, red-green *Crimson King*, a reliable keeper and cooker throughout the winter, and what we called the 'Christmas Apple' which was the unusual *Lord Egremont's Russet* with its tough tawny skin and nutty flavour, which was kept to be eaten as a delicious treat on Christmas Day, or perhaps a selected half-dozen would be given as a special Christmas gift. There was one tree that produced small, hard, apples with an unpleasant, almost peppery flavour which we called cider apples, but the rest of the varieties were unknown and must remain unknown since many of the thousands of varieties of apple which used to exist in England have disappeared forever.

One of the outbuildings was always called 'the shop' because in the nineteenth century the house had belonged to a butcher and this large structure, situated between the end of the house and the road, had indeed been his shop, with at one end a stable for two horses. The floor was made of large, flat, square stones called flagstones or, more confusingly, simply 'flags', which were the usual flooring for houses in those days. Facing the road, the entrance still featured the traditional, double stable-type doors. Why did butchers' shops often have such doors when other shops did not? Maybe, as in stables, it was to allow communication with the outside while at the same time preventing animals from escaping, for until quite recently butchers killed their animals on the premises. The old shop became the workshop and store of the farm. One end was taken up with a large pile of bulging, knobbly, hessian sacks, heaped to the rafters, containing animal feed commonly known as 'cake'. Handling these sacks was not easy, for each one weighed a hundred-weight and a quarter in old measure, or about 140 pounds. Some farms even used sacks whose contents weighed two hundredweights or 224 pounds, but these, known as 'man-killers', are no longer used and you may wonder why they ever were. Inevitably, as children, we climbed on the sacks and it was exciting to be up among the rafters sitting on the rough, dusty, hessian; I wouldn't say this activity was actually forbidden, but rather we were strongly advised not to climb for if we had dislodged a sack it would have been heavy enough to kill one of us or at least break a limb. Of course we carried on when we thought no one was looking. An alternative animal food to the cake was a loose, dry, mixture of various animal feedstuffs known as coarse grazing ration. Among the mixture there were always a few chocolate-brown beans – locust beans I think – about the size of a broad bean, which were a bit hard, but sweet and very chewable and I regularly rifled through the sacks to retrieve these. I sometimes wondered whether the cows too looked forward to finding these rare treats in their troughs and then I felt maybe I was being a little mean by taking them.

Here were kept all the tools that we used in the fields: rakes, peaks and scythes for haymaking; slashers, staff hooks, axes, billhooks, reap hooks, axes and saws for hedging and timber work; large sledgehammers, club hammers, claw hammers, huge pincers and iron bars for fencing; coils of barbed wire and large, dusty, wooden boxes of staples and nails. There were miscellaneous items such as chains and large iron hooks for towing. High up on one whitewashed wall was an old wooden yoke, smoothly carved to fit comfortably on a milkmaid's shoulders and around her neck for carrying buckets of milk to houses in the village, but now disused and worm-eaten. It may have been used also to bring water to the house before mains water was piped to the village. Hanging on a lath and plaster partition from which most of the plaster had long since disappeared were old pieces of horse harness, some old army kit bags and webbing and my grandfather's disused dark blue 'ARP' (Air Raid Protection) helmet and coat, for although he had been too old to be a soldier in the second world war he had volunteered to serve as an air raid warden.

Long before the war, however, once my grandparents had bought the house they set about renting and buying fields as was the local practice to build up a farm. This was mainly driven by my grandmother since my grandfather had his own business which doubtless subsidised the enterprise at first. Meanwhile, my great-grandfather's farm, far from going to the eldest son, was, for the reasons explained earlier, inherited by the unmarried sister and as it was gradually run down my grandmother reassembled its land piece by piece, centred now on her own house, mostly by purchase rather than inheritance. The transfer was largely completed by 1935 when the sister died and in accordance with her will the last field was auctioned and was purchased by my grandfather.

An unusual outbuilding on the farm, and another reminder of how the war had intruded into our little Hardyan world, was what we called 'the shelter'. This was an air raid shelter constructed by my grandfather, drawing on his experience of First World War trench dugouts. He took an active part in local politics and keenly followed current affairs. He knew that the government in the 1930s was extremely pessimistic about the possibility of mounting an effective defence against enemy bombers in the war that was coming. Residents in towns were given little iron huts, called Andersen shelters, to be put in their gardens and covered with soil, where families spent cold and uncomfortable nights during air raids. Being an enterprising and energetic man my grandfather built a luxurious shelter. The walls were about one foot thick, constructed of sheet iron on the outside and wood cladding on the inside; the cavity was filled up with sand. The roof was constructed similarly. There were two blast-shelter doorways, one at each end. About ten feet square on the inside, the room was furnished just like any bedroom with carpets, paraffin lamps and a proper bed. It was truly very cosy. Here my grandmother slept peacefully, and possibly with a false sense of security, during air raids while my grandfather was patrolling the scattered village, checking that no houses showed any light to the bombers, giving reassurance and attending to any incidents, where he sometimes had the gruesome job of clearing up the mangled remains of bodies.

It might be thought that living in deep countryside as we did, the bombers would not have troubled us. But the important city of Bristol was scarcely twenty miles away: a long distance in a horse and cart, but no distance to bombers circling a target or pursued by British fighters and dropping their heavy bombs to speed their escape. Even worse, however, was the presence of a strategic rail junction in the little market town just two miles away. This had been chosen as the location for a large depot of military materiel and was an important target in itself. Photographic surveys by the Royal Air Force showed that in night-time bombing hardly fifty per cent of their bombs fell within three miles of the intended targets. Since German bombers did no better, we were in effect right on the inner circle of their 'bull's-eye'. In a densely built up area the likelihood that a random bomb will hit some house somewhere is of course quite high, but the chance that any particular house will be hit is no

higher than in open country. Bombs killed cows in
the fields, brought down power lines and a house
just a mile away was demolished by a crashing
bomber; no shelter would have survived that. I
remember being in our garden at night, the sky
lit by searchlights, and seeing an enemy bomber
pass over so low that I convinced myself – and
proudly told everyone next day – that I could
see the men's faces inside. Plane crashes were
frequent and at first everyone rushed to see them.
One plane caught fire and the unfortunate crew
could be seen burning in the red-hot framework
of the fuselage. Of course my mother turned me
away quickly and I have no visual memory of
that incident, but for many years after I suffered
from nightmare dreams that I was being burned
alive; my mother always hated to see human
effigies burned on bonfires on Guy Fawkes Night,
and most people were not so keen to see crashed
planes any more.

Just a small selection of the terse entries in
my mother's diary of 1942 is suggestive of those
times.

*20 January. Plane came down behind Heal's and
Puddy's.*

22 January. Snow, stayed home.

14 February. Collected my soap ration.

Everything we bought was rationed and government coupons had to be handed over to the shopkeepers before we could buy anything. This system of rationing lasted until 1951.

18 February. Let mother have four eggs, paid to date.

All produce was by law supposed to be sold to the government for the general good. However, farmyard hens laid erratically and eggs were often exchanged to make up complete dozens for sale.

9 March. Salvage day.

Paper, tins, glass and other materials, known as 'salvage', were collected weekly by the local authority for recycling.for the war effort.

10 March. Cecil left Tobruk for Egypt this week.

In the North African campaign, Tobruk was a strategic city on the Libyan coast. My father was with the Australian garrison when Tobruk held out for five months against an enemy siege in 1941; but, controversially, in a second siege in 1942 it surrendered to the German army.

25 March. Airplane came down right beside Mr Jim Blue's house. Four Australian airmen lost their lives.

30 April. Received coupon book for fowls [hens], 24 lbs [pounds weight] per month.

Food for animals was rationed too. People who were registered producers also put out a bin which the authorities filled twice a week with a fairly disgusting mixture of boiled organic remains called 'swill' for feeding animals.

2 May. Received cheque for War Damage Refund.

6 May. 1 black pullet dead.

A pullet is a young hen which has just started to lay eggs.

8 May. Mother came down at night. Found we had baby rabbits.

Rabbits could be fed entirely with grass and weeds such as dandelions or milk-thistles, gathered from the garden or from roadside verges. Rabbits could also be eaten, so they were free food and many people kept them during the wartime.

11 May. 9 chicks hatched from Mrs Corp's eggs. Cecil stationed 80 miles from Tobruk. Tak[ing] supplies to Tobruk.

I don't know how my mother knew this since all my father's letters were censored, especially details of troop movements.

20 May. 8 eggs sold.

23 May. Letter from Cecil, Egypt post-mark.

15 June. Ploughground 2½ hours.

This sort of entry is quite frequent. In the days before the use of chemical weed control arable crops required a large input of labour for cultivation, singling (thinning) and weeding with hand-hoes. In the war it was 'All hands to the plough' and my mother often helped out for two or three hours in a day.

17 June. Stonemead cut.
Another field mown for hay.

21 June. Lost Tobruk.

27 June. Weston blitzed.
Adjacent to the nearby seaside town of Weston-super-Mare was a large Royal Air Force base with an airfield which was almost certainly the intended target.

28 June. Weston blitzed.

11 July. 5 hours haymaking at Notmoor.
Haymaking, the essential business of conserving the grass for winter feed, had to go on despite all the tragedies, small or large, from the loss of a hen to the loss of Tobruk. While great

nations clashed, the farmers, as peasants have done for centuries, endeavoured to carry on the task of producing food. For as Winston Churchill admitted in his memoirs after the war, his greatest worry during the whole conflict was at the height of the U-boat war when he feared that Britain itself might be starved into surrender. The crisis made a deep impression on the whole nation and strongly influenced the national policy of striving for self-sufficiency in food for three decades after the war.

ℰ/7 Winter Work ℰ℣℣

Winter was a busy time on the farm, but this was not because the days were short, for work extended far beyond the hours of daylight at both ends of the day. Morning milking started and maybe even finished before sunrise; and evening milking extended well beyond sunset at the darkest times of the year. Then there were the extra winter tasks of mucking out the cowshed and washing it down; hay was cut from the great rick and brought in to feed the animals twice a day. The coats of the cows had to be kept clean by combing, washing and clipping to avoid, as far as possible, contaminating the milk. Animals wintered in distant fields were visited daily and hay was cut for them too from the smaller ricks in the fields. Late winter and early spring was the favoured time for calves to be born so that their mothers' milk production could benefit from the first flush of grass; this sometimes meant long hours attending to calving, perhaps in the middle of the night. Calves had to be weaned and fed.

As I have pointed out already, routine work with the animals was not part of my obligation, nor was it my choice, although I might do any of those jobs from time to time as required. Animals, although I liked them well enough, were not what attracted me to farming; I enjoyed what might be called contractor's work. It might be thought that therefore I would have been happier on an arable farm; however, grass, grasslands and haymaking have always held a special attraction for me. Pastoral farming is the most natural form of farming and the visual qualities of flower-rich meadows and the scents of cut grass and hay are much to be preferred to bare soil.[15] Thomas Hardy employs the contrast knowingly to express differing moods in *Tess*.

(i)

January, February and March were the months when the grass was more or less sleeping and there were few animals in the fields; this was the time to prepare the land for the spring and summer growth. All farming depends on sustaining and maybe improving the fertility of the soil, although in what ways and to what level are matters of keen dispute at present. In medieval times fertility was maintained by leaving cultivated land fallow in one year out of two, which was not a very productive system even though all sorts of wastes might be added as well to manure the soil. In the eighteenth century the systematic use of sheep enfolded on fields of turnips and the distribution of manure carried from cattle yards, combined with a regular variation of crops grown, produced enough fertility to enable Britain to feed her growing urban population and so made possible the emergence of the world's first industrial nation. Permanent grassland management is rather different, however, for before the coming of artificial fertilizers there was only the dung of the grazing animals to manure the ground to some extent. Therefore tenancy agreements for the use of grassland often sought to retain the fertility of the land by forbidding the sale of milk or the taking of hay off the grounds, thus limiting activity to grazing for meat production only.

For the truth is that the 'goodness' of milk comes from the grass and ultimately from the soil and must be replaced somehow. Nitrogen is wondrously provided by clover plants growing in mixture with the grasses, and the ability of plants of this family to extract nitrogen out of the air is well-known.[16] The other main nutrient needed is phosphate in some form and this was available then in the form of basic slag or cinder, a waste product from steel production, which also contained lime or calcium, another nutrient and also a great improver of soil texture on clay soils. Providentially the phosphates also encouraged the clover, and over a hundred years ago an agricultural writer described how basic slag 'encourages the growth of clover in an astonishing manner, so that after its application it might almost seem as if clover had been sown'. The main source of fertility, however, was the animal dung itself, stacked behind the cowshed; and although some of its nutrients would be lost during storage it also contained other valuable constituents from the bought-in concentrated feedstuffs.

Various operations were used to keep the permanent grassland in good heart – it will be clear by now that the trouble of ploughing up an established flower-rich meadow and sowing new temporary grass was not an attractive option. These maintenance operations, in addition to manuring, included harrowing, rolling, spreading any dung left by the animals, selective cutting and weeding, cutting back intrusive growth from hedges and paying attention to drainage. Variations in the organisation of grazing and cutting were also important so that, for example, hay was not taken from the same field every year, or grazing could take place at different times of year to encourage a variety of useful grasses.

Undoubtedly the most laborious task was the hauling and spreading of dung.[17] Traditionally the dung was loaded using a 'four sprung peak', also called a dung fork, on to a small, high, two-wheeled wooden wagon called a 'put' or 'putt'. The putt was backed up to the dung-heap for loading and the compacted dung was cut out with an old hay knife. On larger farms there might be three teams of men and putts working together so that loading was almost continuous; but we were doing well if we managed two loads between milkings. This putt was pulled by one horse, although 'down country' where the land was hilly two horses were used in line. The putt was small because dung was heavy and so the load that could be pulled was small. Once in the field a portion of dung was pulled off the back of the little cart with a 'dung hack', a large iron claw on a long handle; then, to the patient and well-trained horse, 'Walk on,' for about seven or eight yards, say ten paces, and stop: 'Whoa!'. About seven little heaps could be made in line from one load and, at a spacing of seven or eight yards, about fourteen loads were needed to cover one acre. These parallel rows of little brown heaps used to be as familiar in the fields in winter as the little heaps of hay, or 'haycocks', awaiting collection were in summer. Now both have disappeared and this laborious system of fertilising the land has been replaced by forklifts and mechanical muck spreaders.

Sometimes dung would be hauled to a distant field, but not spread immediately, and a secondary dung-heap was built up in a corner of the ground. The advantage of this was that it could be done at any time of year; the disadvantage was that some time in winter the dung would have to be reloaded for spreading, thus almost doubling the labour involved. The best conditions for dung hauling were when the ground was firm and hard with frost; wet conditions were difficult for wheeled vehicles and even when early tractors became available some farmers preferred to do this operation using horses. The high axles and large wheels of the traditional putt were designed to cope with deeply rutted unmetalled roads in winter and, although this feature was no longer necessary, it had persisted among the local wagon builders.

The presence of horses was very familiar to me when I was young, although by the time I came to do any serious work they had been replaced by tractors. I remember my cousin and I were sometimes put on the backs of the cart-horses as they were led home after work, just as in those jolly prints of farming in our picture books; except it wasn't quite so jolly. The back of a horse is big, round and smooth and an alarmingly long way from the ground when you are a small person. Being three years older than I was, my cousin always insisted it was her right to be at the front where she could hold onto the horse's mane. I should then have been able to hold on to her, but she usually refused to let me, threatening all sorts of retribution, to which a difference of three years both in seniority and in height gave a certain importance. My situation was therefore rather precarious. I knew she wanted the horse to herself in a childish way, which I can understand, and I knew too that with the heartlessness of a child she would have been rather satisfied to see me fall off. I always felt extremely nervous in this predicament and have never had any wish to ride on a horse ever since.

On another occasion the large black Prince managed to get from the field into the orchard one night and from the orchard he smashed through the little wicket gate into the large vegetable garden where he sampled a little of everything growing there. I remember being overawed at how enormous his hoof prints were everywhere in the soft soil. It was almost as though the devil himself had been there.

I think I was about seven years old when my uncle bought a second-hand tractor, a model known as the Standard Fordson. Thousands of these had been imported from the USA to boost food production during the war. They were powerful and amazingly tolerant of neglect, but they were very slow compared to modern tractors. He also bought a trailer, made in the new way with straight planks and angle-iron and with rubber tyres. The trailer was thus very boxy and modern and some of us felt that a little of the romance went out of farming as the brightly-painted traditional carts with their curved timbers and skilled craftwork were abandoned. We could now carry larger loads of dung although their size was still limited to some extent by the ability of the wet soil to support them and by my uncle's great aversion to seeing deep wheel marks on his precious grassland. No longer could we just say, 'Walk on'. Someone had to climb up into the tractor and drive it on the necessary few yards each time. Then the person behind would shout, 'Whoa,' as though the driver was a horse.

'Dung throwing' was the next stage. We each started on a line of those little heaps and literally threw them around on the grass with the dung forks, trying to get a reasonably uniform coverage. If you were skilled and if the dung was of the right consistency it could be thrown so it scattered quite evenly; you rotated the upper body as you threw, which sprayed the material around (a man spreading gravel will use a similar movement). If you were lucky, large lumps would fly across the grass, breaking up progressively as they went; if not you had to walk around the whole area, which took longer. Thus, although this may appear to have been a simple task, a skilled man with the 'knack' could work much more quickly than could a beginner. The rotating throwing movement was hard on the back after a few acres of this work, especially if a large lump of dung failed to slide off the prongs and brought you up with a jerk. The other hazard was that as you swung around you might inadvertently throw the dung at the man working beside you on the next line – or he at you.

Some people may feel that this must have been

an unpleasant job, but it wasn't. The dung was usually well dried, somewhat like compost, and had rather a sweet smell, like those cow dung fires in India. Working on the grassland on a sunny and frosty winter's day was very pleasant and we knew the work was important; we felt we were feeding the land. A famous agricultural scientist, a professor, once said that his aim in life was 'to make two blades of grass grow where only one grew before'. This apparently simple statement implied an ambitious doubling of the productivity of grassland; its achievement required a lifetime study of plant breeding, chemistry and management of the soil. Possibly we succeeded only in ensuring that at least one blade of grass would grow again where one had grown before, but that was worthwhile. We looked at the even scattering of dung on the grass which was already showing early signs of growth and it looked good.

However, it's clear that this traditional way of distributing many tons of dung in three or perhaps five separate manual operations was laborious and time-consuming. On large mixed farms many men and several teams of horses could be employed for this task, but on a 'one man and a boy' farm, with only a few hours between the necessary milking twice a day, it was not

surprising that dung hauling was not done as often
as it ought to have been done. Nevertheless my
uncle never bought a mechanical muck spreader.
He said the wheels would spoil the grass, for the
early spreaders 'worked off the wheels'; that is,
the machinery was powered by the rotation of
the wheels as they were pulled along and not by
power taken off directly from the tractor as it is
now.

In comparison, spreading basic slag was quite
easy. The spreading rate was only five hundredweights to an acre, thrown from a slow moving
trailer; the main concern was not to spread it too
thickly at first and so have none left before the
whole area was covered; judgement came with
experience. The other problem was how to keep
standing upright on a trailer moving over rough
ground while at the same time shovelling out the
slag. When the tractor was approaching a gutter
the driver would shout a warning, 'Hold on!' and
the shoveller would form a temporary tripod
with his two spread out legs and the shovel. We
never applied nitrogen fertiliser because beyond
a certain level this stimulates the grass to grow
so vigorously that the clover is killed off and its
nitrogen contribution is lost. In the high-input-
high-output systems which are common today

this is accepted and regular doses of expensively manufactured nitrogen compounds are used to produce monocultures of dark green ryegrass. In low-input systems the clover is valued and encouraged. As the world's energy and chemical resources become scarcer and more expensive these natural systems may come back into favour. As I write this I have just noticed an article in the newspaper about the benefits of clover: scientists at the University of Newcastle have shown that milk produced from clover grassland contains 30 to 50 per cent less harmful saturated fat and more of the healthy fatty acids, such as omega-3, compared with inorganically fertilised pastures.

Well into springtime, around Easter, when the soil was firm, the grounds were harrowed. I often wondered about the economics of this, but it was one of my favourite jobs so I never questioned its value. A chain harrow, or harrows, was like an enormous sheet of giant chain-mail armour spread on the ground; it had thick iron spikes on the lower side and was pulled behind two heavy scrapers linked to a horse or to a tractor. Several advantages were claimed for this operation. First it distributed any large lumps of dung left from the throwing and which had not been broken down by frost and rain; and any left by overwintered animals. The dung is a fertilizer but, as my science master never tired of repeating, too much fertilizer, like too much medicine, is a poison. Grass grew vigorously and darkly around the dung, but underneath it the grass was killed and weeds such as docks and nettles were encouraged. Harrowing also spread the molehills, the characteristic spoil mounds which moles throw up as they search for worms to eat. Moles are especially active in spring. As these heaps hardened they became serious hazards for our conventional mowing machines in summer; meanwhile the destruction of those heaps did the moles no harm. Insofar as the heavy harrows crushed the young shoots of grasses these would be encouraged to 'tiller'; that is to branch out to produce more shoots and leaves.

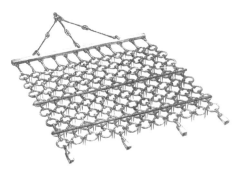

The spikes or 'tines' on the harrows scratched out old matted grass in the sward and so encouraged the finer lower grasses; anyone who has raked and spiked a lawn in spring will understand what we were doing. Some farmers also rolled their fields to firm up the soil, but we felt the land was too wet and heavy for that.

When harrowing was done by use of a horse to pull the harrows these had to be comparatively small and light, for it was continuous hard work for the horse. It was exhausting work too for the man because he had to walk at a brisk pace all day behind the harrows, using a long pair of reins to control the horse. I was doubly fortunate to be able to use the tractor: partly because it was less tiring, but especially because I loved driving. The actions of steering mechanisms and the ingenuity of differential gearing have always fascinated me. As a boy I explored the workings of various types of steering by constructing them in Meccano. At the fun fair or on the seaside pier I spent most of my money on the dodgem cars. One of my dearest wishes was to have a toy pedal car like the ones I eyed covetously in old pre-war editions of *Hobbies Annual*, but instead, like many other boys, I made do with a 'soap-box' cart which I made for myself out of scrap timber and old pram wheels, which undoubtedly provided much more interest and fun and served me over a larger range of my young years. Now, at an early age, I had a real, full size tractor to drive on my own. Today the law does not allow children who are under thirteen years of age even to ride on a tractor.

Steering a car may be fun, but for real interest you have to be able to *see* the front wheels, as on a tractor. As you turn the steering wheel the front wheels suddenly set off in a new direction, eagerly, like a dog straining at his leash, their revolutions eating up the ground. The whole moving geometry of the controlling mechanism of track rods and king-pins and tie-bars happens before your eyes. As you approach the ditch at the edge of the field it is a matter of satisfaction and of judgement to get as close as possible, but once the steering is put over the inevitability of the turning-circle takes over and the driver can only watch in fascination for often it is too late to stop. It is not uncommon in farming for drivers to be crushed or drowned under overturned tractors. There is a tension between the circle being described by the front wheels and the straight-line thrust of the powerful rear driving wheels. On the successful resolution of those forces depends the driver's safety, and possibly his life. If the outside front wheel slips ever so little over the edge of the ditch, or the edge of the ditch has been eroded by cows trying to reach the water, the balance of forces may be dramatically changed in the wrong direction.

I can understand now why my mother always seemed disapproving of my being left alone to do this job, although she never tried to stop me. It was a grand job on the first warm spring days with the friendly drone of the engine and the tinkling of the chain harrow. As I sat sometimes at my studies by my open bedroom window, the sound of a tractor somewhere made me want to be out there driving it; tractors then made an attractive drone or humming noise, unlike the roar of modern tractors, and it called to me. The shapely cast iron seats of traditional farm machinery were surprisingly comfortable and, unlike most tractor driving jobs, when harrowing you didn't have to suffer a stiff neck from looking backwards most of the time at the machinery you were towing, except that is for the satisfaction of seeing the harrows doing their job. As the harrows swept up and down the field, bending the grasses over, alternate dark and light textures were left in the grass as in a well mown lawn; and it was a matter of pride to make these absolutely straight by fixing your eye on some object such as a tree at the far end of the field. This was not solely a matter of pride though: straight lines meant less overlap and an extra ten per cent overlap meant that the job took ten per cent more time. When all was done the tractor was parked under a sheltering hedge and the fuel was turned off, allowing the engine to run itself to a stop. In the sudden stillness it was good to see the field looking so neat and to sense the energy of the reviving grass.

(ii)

After a cow has produced her calf, her milk yield increases for some weeks and then slowly declines until ten months or so after calving she is 'dry'. About two months later, if all is well, she will calve again and the cycle repeats.[18] The falling off in milk production can be controlled partly by regulating her feeding and also by the nature of the milking process. My uncle had one old cow that was always difficult to dry off and he used to say she would go on milking for ever if he let her, although the milk yield at the end would be uneconomic. Perhaps this would be a useful characteristic to breed for since it would save the animals the distress involved in the disposal of their calves.

It was the growth of the grass which determined the wholesale price of milk as set by the Milk Marketing Board; the price received by the farmers was higher in winter when the grass was scarce than it was in the summer. To be set against this was the higher cost of feeding in the winter. Most dairy farmers naturally liked to have some income coming in every month and they managed their herds so that a succession of cows calved throughout the year, but with a peak of calving in late winter to take advantage of the vigorous growth of grass in the spring when there might be more grass than the animals could eat. The arrangement and management of the calving programme is one of the most important aspects of a dairy farmer's job, but it involves regular observation of the animals and it was never my concern.

Like most animals, cows seem to be perfectly capable of giving birth on their own and in summer in the fields often did so. However, a modern dairy cow is not a wild animal, but is the product of breeding over many years to our requirements of form and physiology; problems can arise too when breeds are crossed and the calf is large. In winter, when a cow showed signs – such as restlessness and softening of the pelvic bones – that her calf would be born soon she would be put in the loose-box and watched regularly. If all went well, after some hours the front legs and then the muzzle of the calf would emerge neatly and that was the time to clear the membrane from the nose of the calf. If a leg was doubled back, or even the head, my uncle could usually straighten it out; more than that and it was necessary to call the vet, although like most farmers he resented having to pay the vet's bill, for professional fees in relation to time and trouble appeared to be quite unfairly out of proportion to our normal transactions. It was usual to assist the mother's contractions by pulling on the calf's forelegs; special small ropes, 'calf pulls', with wooden toggles as handles were sold for this job; a rope was looped around each foreleg and we pulled firmly, but I hope not brutally, in time with the mother's efforts. Some people recommend putting the ropes on the calf's neck, the better to help its head through. If after a few contractions no progress was made, but the cow did not seem to be distressed, we sat down and waited a bit. As he smoked my uncle told me he thought that on some farms this pulling was excessive and cruel; men are impatient creatures.

I wondered whether even our interference with nature was really necessary, but birth is a dangerous event and I suppose it was better over as soon as possible before the mother could become exhausted.

When the little calf finally flopped out we checked that its mouth was not obstructed, encouraged it to stand up and took it round to the mother's head, for her instinct is to lick it all over to stimulate its new life. Then it was persuaded to suckle and if it did then all was well for the time being at least.[19] There is nothing that looks quite as clean and bright as a newborn calf, especially if it is black and white, yet all its substance, from its pink nose and glossy coat to its tiny tail, has been formed from the grass.

Traditional dairy farming was a fairly humane activity in most respects, conforming as it did to natural rhythms, but the system produced more calves each year than the farmer needed to keep up his herd. The birth of the calf is of course necessary to stimulate the mother to produce her milk. The best calves, or rather those from the best mothers, might be kept and raised as replacements to have their own calves in a couple of years' time.[20] A good herd in this way was built up over many years and consisted

of grandmothers, mothers and daughters each
individually reared, which is one reason why
their slaughter in an epidemic is so devastating
an experience for a farmer. Most calves however
were taken from their mothers within a few days
or weeks and when they had been weaned on to
solid foods they were sold at market for a few
pounds, perhaps equal to a workman's weekly
wage for a good heifer calf, although this was by
no means all profit, but much less for a bull calf.
The mother would call, perhaps all night, for her
lost calf with a characteristic sound – 'bawling'
as we called it – and if in a field she would run up
and down, frantically searching.

Some people thought this was cruel; my
mother certainly did and I don't think my uncle
was happy about it, but it was accepted as a
necessity.[21] I think we got as close to cruelty free
farming as possible and it was certainly far better
than the factory farming which is tolerated today
just because people will not pay a fair price for
food, although they are happy to waste money on
all sorts of consumer junk. After all, in the wild,
in nature, calves would be taken by wolves or by
large cats; nature is very profligate with its young
and even among those animals and birds which
survive predators, many die of starvation and cold

in winter. I always find it curious that people who condemn organised hunting are often the same people who appear to enjoy watching TV 'nature' programmes as animals are hunted, tormented and eaten alive by predators. We were not hunt supporters; we resented the often arrogant attitudes and behaviour of some huntsmen and women. But I care about the physical suffering of animals and it seems to me that the hounds do no more to the fox than the fox does to a rabbit when he can; whereas having grown up in the country I have absolutely no doubt that shooting and the effects of shooting are often far more cruel. Thomas Hardy knew that too as he shows in *Tess*.

By now undoubtedly I have offended all sides in this debate, which is perhaps only to say that we are all complicit in one way or another. Some people say animals have no feelings, only instincts, yet we know that it is precisely those experiences associated with our instincts that can cause most pain to men and women. Any sympathetic person who works closely with animals will be in little doubt that they can experience rejection, loss – whether of companions or familiar environment – and maybe even embarrassment. Increasingly scientists think that our feelings are controlled by chemistry; it seems likely that animals have a similar chemistry; indeed many animal experiments in behavioural psychology are based on that assumption. So we might at least suppose that the ways in which we treat animals will sometimes cause them to experience a profound sense of unease even if it is only a deep chemical disturbance. I sometimes think that animals may in fact experience 'feelings' rather more intensely than we do; that the feelings they experience may be likened to bright primary colours whereas our own are like modulated tones, for the animals are unable to moderate their distress as we do by recourse to the sympathy of poetry or music or even simply of conversation, especially when they are condemned to live in solitary confinement. But after all, 'they are only animals'.

✒8 Some Winter Jobs ✒

(i)

Making spars for thatching used to be a trade in itself. Thomas Hardy's constant heroine in *The Woodlanders*, Marty South, earned an honest living that way. Hardy seems to imply it was an unusual occupation for a woman, presumably because strong hands were needed. My uncle, in keeping with his independent and self-sufficient approach to his farming, not only thatched his own ricks, but made his own spars for the work.

His parents, my grandparents, lived in the farmhouse; uncle had his own house a few hundred yards up the road. Although the land appeared to be quite flat, up the road and down the road had exact meanings: down was towards the sea; up was the opposite direction; it was obvious to us, but often confused summer visitors. When directed to 'go down the road' to the Post Office they would look in confusion at the flat, straight, road going off in both directions. As children we argued, as children do, about the seeming lack of logic, but came to accept the convention. My uncle's house was late nineteenth century, built on the traditional 'square house' plan, and had a large garden, paddock and orchard. The house had once belonged to a professional man, an architect – or an 'archie-tek' as some called him. A series of old brick outbuildings ran from the kitchen and back door down one side of the garden and these were adapted to farm work and to the storage of smaller items. It was here that uncle made his spars.

As you entered his back door you could turn left into the central passage which led to all the downstairs rooms of the house or go straight ahead into a small dairy, or you could turn right into the range of ancillary buildings: the first was a scullery and the second, with heaps of coal and logs on the floor, a fuel store with other spaces beyond. Many years before, presumably from an alteration job somewhere, the architect had salvaged a number of very large and beautifully cut and engraved glass panels which stated in ornate letters 'Grand Hotel' although they did not say where the hotel was or perhaps had been. The architect had employed these panels to keep heat in the house, and dust out of it, by partitioning the main house from the other spaces. Incongruously, you went through the old doors of the Grand

Hotel into a space which at first sight was rather like one of those gloomy and slightly creepy *tableaux morts* which are now displayed in many museums and historical tourist attractions, with their station-tannoy voices, electric mock-candles and dust.

Except that this space was not dead, but alive and above all cosy: sweet-smelling chips of fresh willow were heaped on the uneven brick floor; light was provided by the real and steady flame of a paraffin hurricane lamp – the famous *feuer hand* brand from Germany – hanging from a wrought iron hook on a rafter, while another lamp stood on a shelf and gave light over my uncle's shoulder. He sat on an old and simple Windsor chair as he worked and I sat on a large up-ended log which was used as a chopping block for cutting up small 'lighting fire stuff' or for splitting small logs for the house. And as usual we talked, on and off. There was no heating, though the lamps gave some warmth, both in reality and – not unimportantly – in the imagination; we wore warm woollen clothes as everyone did in those times for most houses were scarcely less draughty than the proverbial barn and the only heating in them, if any at all, a single fire at one end of the room.

Several bundles of sticks, bound with rough

tangy binder twine, were propped against a wall. Clearly these were not ordinary sticks to be used on a fire for they were more or less uniform in shape and size: nearly three and a half feet long and about an inch in diameter. Uncle selected a bundle, laid it down and cut the sisal twine so the sticks spilled tidily onto the floor. These were 'spar gads', young shoots of 'withy' or 'widdy' – the local names always used for the pollard willows which grew along the field boundaries. He selected one gad and examined it carefully, although he would use them all and had already made his selection as they were harvested; they were going to be split right along their length so it was important that there were no large side shoots or knots. If knots were present it was easier to make the split at right-angles to them rather than in the same plane; which was the reason for the examination.

All timbers split most easily when 'green', that is when the sap is still in the wood. When they are freshly felled very large oak logs can easily be split with a few wedges and a 'beetle' or large hammer, but this is impossible later. When sawing was done laboriously by hand, splitting in this way was much preferred as a method of converting timber for all but the finest work. The result is pleasingly picturesque and strong and is most commonly seen in traditional cleft oak fencing, especially in south-east England. The gads had been cut from the trees only a few days or weeks before.

Billhook

Splitting was done with a special small billhook. A billhook is like a butcher's cleaver but as its name suggests it has a hooked end which is indispensable for grabbing brambles and branches when trimming hedges. The wide flat hook also adds weight to the distal end of the blade and so increases the momentum of a stroke. Old catalogues show these hooks were supplied in a large range of sizes and of variations on the basic design; over thirty different ones are shown. Some were large and clumsy, meant for heavy work; others, small and fine, or 'sweet', were for delicate jobs such as spar making. Each workman had his own favourite. The hook my uncle was using he called 'a sweet little hook' for there was affection for good tools and a pleasure when you held them.

He picked up a gad and held it under his left arm. The hook was razor-sharp, 'whetted', or sharpened, with a fine stone; you could shave the hairs off the back of your hand with it. He placed the sharp edge on the end of the gad and wiggled the blade slightly, working it towards his body and into the wood which began to split lengthwise. The splitting was done as much by the leverage of the blade as by cutting, and he moved the blade to left or right as required to keep the split running true down the centre of the gad. It looked easy, but it wasn't. If the gads were considered to be thick enough he might split them again into quarters.

When he had split forty or so gads into eighty or more he pointed their ends sharply with a few deft slashes of another hook, for the sweet little hook was kept for its one job only. This pointing was not done on the wooden chopping block as most people would choose to do, but by firmly holding the gad vertical and slashing downwards with a sharp hook, rather as a pencil is sharpened with a penknife, for each blow of the hook on the block was unnecessary wear on the cutting edge. By the end of the evening's work the floor was covered by the sweet-smelling chips of willow, shining white in the light of the hurricane lamp, a scene very like that described by Hardy. The chips would later be used for the fire.

Herbert Edlin tells us in his book *Woodland Crafts* that at this stage the spars were bundled up and sold as they were and he includes photographs which show the bundles being prepared. Before they can be used, however, the spars must be bent into their hairpin shape; Edlin says the bending was done by the thatcher as he selected each new spar. This is puzzling since the willow, and the hazel used elsewhere in the country, as it dries loses its pliability and soon becomes brittle. An expert in building conservation tells me the spars are soaked in water to make them pliable before the thatcher bends them, but it would seem so much more logical for the spars to be bent by the spar maker.

My uncle always bent his spars as he made them, while the wood was still green, for they would not be used until autumn, nine or ten months away. A special knack, which I never quite mastered, was required for bending. He gripped the prepared spar at its mid-point with two hands close together and twisted the timber once or twice to separate the fibres without breaking them; then he rotated his wrists so that the spar was bent around his forefingers. This was where strong hands were needed; but if Edlin was right, Marty South may not have needed such strong hands after all. This bend was not a single 180 degree bend, which anyone could make, which might snap the spar; somehow it consisted of two bends of 90 degrees close together with a little straight bit between them. This meant that the spar could accommodate the thickness of the horizontal willows, known as stretchers, which were laid over the reed on the rick while at the same time the two points of the spar could be brought together to be thrust into the rick. Bends were always made with the bark of the willow on the outside where the fibres were younger and more elastic. Fibres on the inside were sometimes bruised beforehand by a blow with the back of the hook to ease the bending.

About a hundred spars were used in thatching a small rick. Hardy says, and no doubt he had done his homework, that Marty South could make 1500 spars, unbent presumably, in 'a day and half a night'; this would have required the splitting and pointing of about 750 gads in that time which I find a little difficult to believe. There is little or no demand for spars in agriculture now, although a few are used in house thatching which fortunately has been revived from near extinction. But a hundred years ago nearly all the country's vital winter store of animal fodder in the form of hay, and most of the corn harvest too, was protected by the use of these simple yet essential devices on innumerable ricks all over the land. I feel privileged to have been part of that *tableau vivant* and a little sad that I can never again experience it in all its genuineness and reality.

(ii)

Moles as such are harmless animals. They don't slaughter chicken nor do they eat valuable crops; but the results of their excavations in search of worms for food can be a great nuisance as anyone will know whose garden has been taken over by a mole. Spoil heaps appear on well kept lawns, tunnels collapse underfoot and the mole's progress under flower beds is marked by lines of wilting plants. In farming, the soil put up by the mole can render a significant part of the grass area unfit for grazing animals. Moles are voracious feeders. I was told when young that if I kept a mole as a pet (unlikely) I would have to feed it every three hours day and night or it would die. A mole is like a velvety torpedo with cylindrical body, pointed nose, tiny almost blind eyes, but with short powerful claws which enable it almost to swim through the soil, zooming around underground in its search for prey. A single mole can devastate a garden in a few days.

Mole Heaps in a Pasture in March
'The soil put up by the mole can render a significant part of the grass area unfit for grazing animals.'

Annual chain harrowing is only a temporary cure for the nuisance of the molehills in the grass, for the mole is active all year round. Unfortunately the only solution is to kill the mole and in the past the methods used to do this were extremely cruel. I am always puzzled by the ordinariness of cruelty: how apparently nice people seem incapable of empathising with physical pain; how civilisations that we admire for their great art and literature carried out unspeakable actions. I read recently that a gene for empathy has been discovered; this gene allows neurones in our own brain to reform so as to replicate the feelings and experiences of others; this gene is also important in the transmission of physical skills. Not everyone has this gene, which doesn't surprise me. Those who do have it will instinctively campaign against cruelty and others may then be convinced by pure argument.

Mole traps operated in the same way as the man traps used against poachers by landowners in the nineteenth century; they were triggered when the animal, or man, stepped on to a metal plate. The much smaller mole traps were placed in a mole burrow or 'run' and when the animal passed over the trigger plate powerful springs were released so that iron jaws squeezed the life out of its soft body or, in another version, iron spikes were thrust through it. It was a painful and lingering, almost unimaginable, death.

Hanging on the whitewashed wall of my uncle's barn was one of each kind of trap, well out of the reach of children's hands – and there they stayed, forever unused. As children we passed them everyday and sometimes gazed at them in awed fascination; they were in an almost biblical sense unclean, an abomination; but it was only as I grew older that I developed the facility to comprehend their reality. My uncle was a humane man on the whole, but even if he had wanted to use the traps my grandmother would never have allowed it. Incredibly, despite all the modern concern for animal welfare and the banning of cruel traps for rabbits, mole traps of the first type are still widely and cheaply available for use.

Patience and alertness were necessary qualities for my uncle's much more humane method of catching moles. He said the best time to find a mole at work was in the early morning, although they can be seen making their mounds, or 'heaving' as we called it, at any time of day and all year round. The best time of year perhaps was the winter or early spring, before they had their young. In winter, too, the ground was water-logged; the moles then burrowed just beneath the surface of the ground and the raised lines of their burrows could easily be seen, as in some Disney cartoon. In fact rarely will you see the mole itself; just the soil being pushed aside or thrown up in the centres of the spoil heaps.

As we came close to the area where clearly the mole had been active my uncle told me to walk very slowly and softly, putting each foot flatly onto the soil, for a mole is very sensitive to vibrations and will stop work when it feels someone approaching. We looked around for the most recent mounds; these we could distinguish by the slightly darker tone of their damp fresh earth; then for the main tunnel leading to these current workings.[22] We saw earth being pushed up through one of the mounds; the mole was there all right; could we avoid disturbing it before we were ready?

Approaching his selected tunnel cautiously, my uncle suddenly stamped his foot hard down through the thin covering of turf, blocking the mole's return route. The busy mole, suddenly sensing the tremor in the ground, shot back along his extended tunnel – and ran smack into uncle's boot. Uncle bent down, picked up the squirming mass of black velvet from the loose soil and tapped its nose sharply against the side of his

boot. Despite the mole's strength in burrowing
it has a surprisingly tender nose; that one blow
killed it instantly as surely as a blow to the back
of the neck kills a rabbit.

I have several times used a variant of this
method in gardens. If possible start early before
the maze of burrows becomes too complex. Poke
around in a tunnel or in a mound until your fingers
feel the edge of the burrow; then put the end of
a garden hose down the hole, turn on the water
and watch. Soon a mole will pop up out of the
ground like a diver coming up for air. Grab him
quickly and hold him firmly around his middle or
he will rapidly bore down through the soil again.
It is a wise precaution to wear leather gloves since
moles have very sharp teeth.

What to do now? Put the animal in a bucket
where he will run around in a fine old temper and,
to the surprise of most people who think the mole
is a silent creature, make a lot of noise. You could
dispatch him with a quick blow as described, but
if you are tender-hearted you might take him to
the country and let him go. Of course it would
be unneighbourly to release him near another
person's garden, although it is surprising what
some people will do to increase their chances
in the local flower show or a 'best kept garden'

competition. I don't know whether moles have a homing instinct, but I once released one half a mile up the road and it was back the next day. I think it was the same one for recently an amateur lady scientist has won a prize for demonstrating that even the humble garden snail can find its way back to a garden from several hundred yards away.

Mole catching, like spar making, was once a trade in itself. The mole catcher would be called in by big farmers to deal with infestations of moles; old photographs show how the catcher would hang the dead bodies along a fence by a road as a grisly advertisement of his competence. Sometimes the velvety furs were sold to be made into garments.

(iii)

Pollarding the willows could be done at any
time of year according to the current need for
their product, but like most forestry and pruning
work it was best done in the winter. We never used
the term pollarding; I'm not sure we even knew
what it was. 'Shrouding' was the word: 'shroudin'
withies'. It's a curious word and seems to have no
connection with the usual meaning of that term
which is to cover something, usually a dead body,
with a cloth. Or it could mean 'shredding'; the
Anglo-Saxon words for both are similar

One February morning we saw that there had
been a fog and then a frost overnight and the twigs
of the dormant willows were decorated prettily
with glassy white pearls of ice. We parked the car
by the moss-covered five bar gate and carried the
ladders and tools into the field. The first willow
was just inside.

'You start,' said uncle and with the enthusiasm
of youth I laid the short ladder against the crown
of the old willow, climbed up with the small axe
in my hand and selecting a convenient branch
dealt it a mighty blow at its base. The whole tree
quivered and dozens of ice pearls dropped into
the open neck of my shirt and slid coldly down
my back. Uncle's previous enigmatic smirk gave

An overgrown Pollard Willow

way to a burst of laughter at my discomfort and I quickly realised he had known what would happen. I could see the humour in it and no harm was done; worse things happen in the world of work and if they are not too extreme and are accepted lightly and in good humour they produce a valuable camaraderie. He showed me how next time in frosty weather I should first shake the tree with the ladder.

Willow branches had many uses in the local rural economy, similar to those of hazel in other parts of the country. Every farm had dozens of pollard willows, which is an indication of how they were valued then. The smallest stems were used as pea-sticks for peas to climb up in the garden; larger ones could be used to support runner beans. We would have thought it very odd to spend money buying bamboo sticks for our beans. Withies could also be woven into hurdles, but these had little use in our sort of farming since they were too flimsy to control cows; hurdles were traditionally used in sheep farming to form temporary enclosures. We didn't even call them hurdles, but 'withy-rush hedges' and their use was more domestic: to contain fowls or ducks or alternatively to protect gardens from small animals. Spars and runners for thatching have been described already, but the

Willows after Pollarding

main agricultural use for withies in the larger sizes was as fence posts. Willow is not a long lasting or durable timber, but it was readily available and free; it also had the property of easily taking root so a fence post might grow, which extended its life indefinitely, and it could even form a new tree to be one day shrouded in its turn.[23] Most withies, however, when they were dry and had served a purpose – and many which had not – became excellent and abundant firewood. In the modern jargon, they were our bio-fuel.

Quite commonly the main trunks or boles of the willows were very old; just how old was often impossible to know since the centres with their chronologies of growth rings had long ago rotted away completely, leaving only part-open tubes of thin live tissue – the cambium – sandwiched between the bark and a little remaining wood. Repeated pollarding caused the trees to grow large clumps or crowns at their tops and it was from these crowns that fresh shoots in profusion sprouted with surprising vigour. Some of these crowns were like miniature gardens. Green mosses crept among the young shoots; in the moss grew the common polypody fern or, in summer, the pink flowers of Herb Robert. There might be a bird's nest; in one large willow we even discovered that a fox had made a temporary lair. In others, however, were nettles and brambles which had to be cleared before cutting could begin.

Although there were similarities, each crown presented a unique combination of problems since the shoots were so thick that each one interfered with the cutting of those next to it. Of course I tried to work in from the outside, but that wasn't always as straightforward as it sounds for the outside branches often grew low down on the crown which involved swinging the little axe upwards against its own weight while I was hanging half off the ladder; it was safer to hold on to the tree with my left hand and not to the ladder itself which might slip. The ladder had to be placed at various angles, some rather unsafe, and was often moved around with a jerking movement to save going down and up again; you

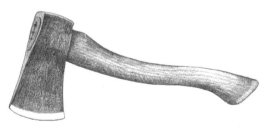

Small Axe

put one hand on the tree and the other on the ladder and lifted it and yourself and swung it to its new position. Some people favoured using a small saw; others a billhook. I preferred the small axe or hatchet, but whatever the tool it had to be used at all sorts of improvised angles. It was a matter of pride and good workmanship to cut the new shoots right down to the crown; although this was more difficult it was also common sense since any stumps left sticking up would make cutting even more problematic next time and probably wound our hands as we chopped. A newcomer to the village pollarded some willows in his garden and left all the stumps six inches long. 'Townie' we said to ourselves contemptuously as we went by. Clearly he had used a saw and no doubt discovered he couldn't work it low down among the maze of branches.

Beginners favoured the saw because they could buy a new sharp blade for a bow saw or get a panel saw sharpened by the old deaf carpenter in the village. Again, these things cost money whereas a small axe and a whetstone for sharpening it would last a lifetime. Every craft that uses edge tools requires for its success that those tools be expertly sharpened; and every tool has its own way of being sharpened whether it is the woodsman's heavy axe or the delicate tool of the woodcarver making a memorial for the village church. The carver's gouge, the wood-turner's chisel, the wagon maker's planes, the reaper's hook, the hedger's bill, the mower's scythe: all had their own shapes and angles known to those who earned their living from their tools.

When the sharp edge of an axe becomes blunted with use it is a great mistake to freshen it quickly by making the angle a little more obtuse; you must take a little more time and 'whet' it back keeping to the original angle. Of course when the edge has been made obtuse in this way it can be made more acute again by grinding and when this was done with large, slow, water-cooled grindstones turned by hand it was not a big problem, except that you would not have a grindstone with you in the field. But modern high-speed electric grindstones can quickly overheat the thin metal of the cutting edge and draw its temper away so that it will never 'take' a fine edge again. It is a remarkable thought that, theoretically at least, the extreme edge of a fine chisel should be only one atom of iron thick, although if you examine it under a powerful lens it will look like a jagged row of rocks. I know a sculptor whose work, while successful, could not be described as fine;

he sharpens his chisels on an electric grindstone and makes the sparks fly in showers and wonders why his tools are never sharp. It is better to carry a small whetstone and touch up the edge of your axe regularly so it doesn't get out of shape.

On a Saturday morning, in fresh early sunshine, I would sharpen the little hand-axe with a whetstone, working on the large stone windowsill outside the kitchen. The sill was so large that it served as a shelf for small tools and a variety of pots and tins, and sometimes, as now, as a workbench. I took time to get the angle right and the edge near razor-sharp. Many people think they can't use tools, but that is because they don't sharpen them properly. No one can work with blunt tools. My mother watched as I set off across the fields with a ladder on my shoulder, the stone in my pocket and the axe in my hand. She knew that if a blow of the axe slipped off target and injured me, so easy in the confusion of a pollard willow tree, I would be too far away to call for help.

It was reckoned that an average withy whose young shoots or 'poles' were six or seven years old and between one and three inches thick should be shrouded in about fifteen minutes and I found this was achievable, for most poles could be severed with a few slicing cuts and some with just one. If I had to pull out the cut stuff myself and bundle it up then it took longer. As the poles were cut they fell with a creak and a swishing sound in a graceful arc and ended upside down with their twigs resting on the grass or in the hedge and their freshly cut butts resting around the crown of the withy. Gradually a tree became encased in a sort of tent of cut poles and I could see from where, perhaps, the term shrouding had come.

For fencing material the poles were not cut until they were from three to six inches thick and these took longer for they were like small trees all growing from the top of another tree. At this size the weight of the growing poles begins to put a deal of strain on the old trunks which can become split and twisted and they may even fall over. In our lowland river valleys such as the Thames Valley there are many pollards which have been allowed to become grossly overgrown; this unfortunately tempts the river authorities to remove them altogether before they can fall over and block the watercourses in winter, but it doesn't seem to be worth anyone's labour to pollard these trees and sell the poles to gardeners rather than import exotic bamboos.

With a final trim of the stumps to ensure that

no untidy and dangerous spikes were left on the crown, I removed the ladder and pulled down all the branches, laying them out on the grass in parallel bundles. I then tied them with 'withy bonds' as my uncle had shown me. To make a withy bond you select a long branch about one inch thick at most, grasp the twiggy end and whirl the thick end around in the air so that the twigs become twisted into a sort of rope in your hands. You can then make a loop in the 'rope' with a single half-hitch knot. Slide the stout end under a bundle and wrap the bond around it; then put the end through the loop and pull it tight by kneeling on the bundle. The end is then bent back and thrust under the bond. Two or three of these bonds each would contain the bundles securely for carting back to the farmyard. This must have been the traditional way for many centuries and although the binder twine used in mechanical corn binders and, increasingly, baler twine were becoming widely available we found it satisfying to use the old way; and bits of string left about would have been another hazard for the cows.

Back in the farmyard the bundles were piled high against a tall hawthorn hedge in the orchard. As children we had naturally enjoyed climbing and bouncing and tumbling on these, for everything was our playground. Now the withies were to be sorted and cut out for their various uses. This was usually done by my grandfather who taught me how quickly a series of flicks with a very sharp billhook can remove the small side branches and point the end of a pole while it is held suspended in the air and turn it into a useful bean-stick.

Beside my grandmother's little knot garden a large pollard sycamore had inappropriately grown up. I don't why my grandfather didn't remove it, except that in the tangle of ivy in its crown a blackbird nested every year and he loved to hear a blackbird sing on early summer evenings. One year he asked me to pollard his sycamore and produced a very old ladder for the job. It was the one with the dead knot halfway up so we made sure that was on top, but its condition had become even worse over time. The rungs were badly eaten by woodworm and two were missing. He explained that to avoid breaking any more as I climbed up I should place my feet close to the sides of the ladder and not on the middle of the rungs where the stress would be greater; how practically we learned our mechanics. I managed to get to the top safely (or perhaps dangerously) and started work. The branches had grown to the size of fence poles; the heavy butt of one, as I finally cut through it, slipped off the crown and bounced right down the ladder, knocking out every rotten rung except one at the top and two at the bottom. How should I get down? I suggested to my grandfather that he might fetch another ladder, but he said I could slide down the remaining sides of the ladder, which I did like a toy monkey on a stick and with no harm. He was not at all unmindful of my safety: indeed he always advised caution and patience where he considered necessary; he merely thought it was a situation that I should be able to deal with. He was however a little put out by the loss of a ladder which he felt, had I not been so careless, could have served for a few more years.

9 The Milk Factory

Taking milk to the milk factory was a daily job, seven days of the week and every day of the year. This was the true harvest of a dairy farm and its regularity symbolised both the routine drudgery and the security of dairy farming. The milk factory located by the railway line four miles away was part of the Wiltshire United Dairies group, always referred to as 'Wilts United' as though it were perhaps a football team. Wilts United lorries and their drivers provided a pick-up service for the daily stacks of milk churns, but most farmers preferred to take their milk themselves. I don't think this was only to save money on collection fees, but because the farmers liked to watch to make sure there was no mix-up and that the measure was fair as their precious milk was checked and sampled by inspectors at the factory.

Milk was, almost literally, money. It was the custom then for many farms to make their own cider from their own orchards and the cider rooms were dark mysterious places dominated by the great screws and beams of the cider presses which resembled some great medieval machine, which I suppose in effect they were. These dens contained old wooden benches and dusty hessian sacks and fat-bellied wooden barrels; there were no licensing hours and no duty was payable since the product was not technically spirits, although many people have been taken unawares at the potency of young cider. I sometimes had to go through the yard or 'barton' of the farm opposite to get access to some fields and the barton gate was right beside the doorway to the cider room. Whatever the time of day there seemed to be men in there quietly drinking cider, which with the self-consciousness of youth I found rather intimidating; I wondered also whether they ever did any work in the middle of the day. A caller to a farm on business would usually be invited to partake. My uncle liked to point out the paradox that the market price of a pint of cider was much more than that of a pint of milk, yet if a visitor who was offered cider had said he would prefer milk it would be seen as most offensive; I suppose it was as though someone offered to buy you a coffee and you said you would prefer to have the money. Milk was money.

Each morning before breakfast – and breakfast was at ten-thirty, after five hours of work – the churns of milk from the morning and previous evening's milkings were wheeled around from the dairy to stand at the side of the road. A churn was made of thick metal to withstand rough use; I'm not sure what they weighed, but I have discovered that an aluminium churn weighed just over thirty pounds and the steel ones must have weighed more. A gallon of milk weighed maybe ten pounds and each churn held ten gallons. The old-fashioned conical Victorian 'railway-platform' churns held sixteen gallons; they had become very rare, but we did occasionally use them. Even ten-gallon churns when full were very heavy and unlike most heavy loads they could not be handled carelessly; they had to be kept upright and could not be dropped or the precious milk would be lost. They were awkward to handle, for the handles were right at the top and you had to get your arms up very high to lift the base onto a stand or onto a truck. In fact the churns were never filled to more than six or seven gallons capacity which was quite enough to lift on to the trailer and then up onto the chest-high platform at the factory.

Churns were moved around by 'rolling'. The lids were deep and fitted very firmly; they had a substantial downwardly-curving rim. A cupped hand fitted very comfortably on to this rim and I often wondered whether the lids had been designed with this in mind. By tilting the churn a little, first making sure the lid was tight, and gripping the rim of the lid, the churn could be rolled along with a sort of steering-wheel motion of the hands. This may not seem very remarkable, but it's more difficult than it looks and certainly my attempts were very slow and clumsy at first as the base tried to roll away from me and the whole thing seemed likely to tip over. But regular workmen became amazingly skilful: they could nonchalantly roll a churn along at fast walking pace using only one hand; some could even roll two churns at once, one each side, which showed an impressive degree of coordination since the balance of each churn needed constant tending.

Milk was difficult to transport over long distances in the days before mechanical transport; and without refrigeration it became 'sour' and unhealthy within a few hours. Therefore, in the nineteenth century, herds of cows were kept in all cities and large towns; fresh milk was distributed locally by milkmaids and milkmen who each carried two buckets suspended from wooden shoulder yokes. It was usual for householders to boil the milk to preserve it as soon as it was delivered, for pasteurisation or commercial heat treatment before sale was not introduced until after the Second World War. My mother always boiled or 'scalded' the milk in hot or thundery weather since we received our supply direct from the farm.

Milk Churn

In the 1870s an outbreak of disease among the cows of London, combined with the great growth of the railways which had taken place, led to a switch to rural production. 'Creameries' or milk factories were established which received milk from local farms and distributed it in bulk to the towns. Essential to this trade was the milk churn. The name comes from the churns in which butter was made by agitating or 'churning' the milk. By the 1970s the Milk Marketing Board insisted on bulk storage and collection of milk for all farms and the familiar milk churn disappeared. It had lasted just one hundred years.

Naturally there was mutual interest in how many churns of milk other farmers produced each day. You never knew of course how full they were, but fluctuations in number were noted. 'Farmer House has eleven churns and we only have six.' 'All out of the cake bag, old boy,' uncle would reply contemptuously, meaning that the farmer relied too much on bought-in feed and not on the grass, which was not proper farming in my uncle's opinion. In this daily display of churns farmers were torn between the two tendencies of wishing to appear to be good at their work and, on the other hand, not wishing to appear too prosperous so they could attempt to plead poverty when driving a bargain. Everyone knew the price of milk and here on public display was a farm's complete annual turnover. I remember thinking that five half-filled churns of milk each morning seemed to be such a disproportionately small return from eighty or so acres of grassland and all the work that we put into those acres. It was a lesson in how hardly our food is won, a lesson which it seems we must learn afresh in every generation and may have to learn again now commodity prices are rising steeply once more in 2011.

After delivery to the factory, disagreements sometimes arose about the quality of the milk, but a farmer was at a considerable disadvantage here. Before the milk was sent off he had to attach a milk label to each churn. On this label was written the farmer's name, the number of the churn and the number of churns in each batch. A vertical metal scale on the outside of each churn was marked in gallons, but since the churn was not transparent this measure did not enable a very precise estimate to be made of the contents, although on some churns the marks were raised in the metal and on the inside you could see and feel a corresponding small hollow. Otherwise the measure could be taken only by using a stainless steel rod, preferably sterilised by being wiped with sodium hypochlorite or 'bleach'. Farmers would use a stainless steel dipper on a long handle to transfer milk as necessary to make the contents exact gallons, which saved argument at the factory. My uncle also, quite legitimately, transferred creamy milk from one churn to another less creamy in order to make sure that all met the minimum standard for butterfat content, for this was where serious problems arose.

Samples were taken from each churn as it arrived at the milk factory and analysed later by the laboratories there. If the minimum standard for butterfat content was not reached the milk fetched a lower price or it could be rejected completely. Although a farmer could, for a fee, have the quality of his milk independently tested it was not possible to test a particular churn after the event since its contents had already been bulked with others at the factory. When milk was below standard, warning letters were sent out and if this happened several days in succession the situation caused despondency and also bad feeling since the factory already had taken the milk which the farmer might have used for feeding calves or pigs. It was as though you had worked hard for a week only to be told that your work was no good and you would not be paid. I see from a website that a farmer in Minnesota is claiming that when he disputed the discrepancy between his own test results over a period and those of the state collection agency, the agency threatened to refuse to accept his milk; and England in the 1950s was a much more deferential society than the USA is now.

It was illegal to sell milk with less than three per cent butterfat content, although I suppose that if someone knowingly chooses to buy skimmed or semi-skimmed milk today that is acceptable. This law was brought in at the beginning of the twentieth century to counter the notorious 'watering' of milk: that is the addition of water to increase the apparent volume of milk that could be sold. Milk is over eighty-seven per cent water anyway so the remaining thirteen per cent of solids is crucial to its nutritional value, although a little extra water is unlikely to be noticed. At the end of the nineteenth century the Society of Chemical Analysts had decreed that milk with less than the requisite three per cent should be assumed to have been 'adulterated' whether by addition of water or by removal of cream or 'the top of the milk'. After much debate the Board of Agriculture in 1901 supported this stand unless the contrary could be proved by the seller, which as pointed out above is difficult to do after the event. This assumption seems to have gone against fundamental principles of English common law such as the presumption of innocence until guilt is proved and, too, the question of intent.

Following some unfair prosecutions the Board acknowledged that under certain conditions a herd may naturally produce milk which is below standard and so instructed the local councils which were responsible for checking standards to arrange for samples to be taken at the time and place of milking before considering a prosecution for adulteration. It can be seen that this situation was also potentially unfair. Testing after the event did not prove anything about the original sample and if the quality of the milk improved by the second test this might even have suggested that the original milk had indeed been adulterated. To some extent regular independent testing was and is an answer, although not it seems for that farmer in Minnesota who has decided to give up farming altogether. Unfortunately, even if a farmer was not guilty of malpractice, the dairy was not obliged to accept milk which didn't meet its standards. On the other hand, taking some cream from the top of the churn was technically adulteration even though the remaining milk might be up to standard. I know that my grandmother surreptitiously took a half pint or so when she thought my uncle wasn't around. If she heard him coming she would scuttle away and he would appear and glance about like a stage villain with a dark scowl on his face; I'm sure he knew, but he never complained when she served him cups of tea with thick creamy milk which was the way he liked it.

What was a farmer to do who had problems with butterfat content? Contrary to what might be supposed, increased feeding has little or no effect on butterfat content and may even make matters worse by increasing the volume of milk produced; indeed the problem is most likely to occur in spring and early summer when the grass is most abundant. There is no quick fix and good practice and long term management are essential. The quality of milk naturally falls off after the third month of lactation, which partly explains the fall off in late summer, and also shows the desirability of having a succession of calving throughout the year. Some animals, and some breeds, constitutionally produce better quality milk so their peak production also should be spread throughout the year. The cattle should be kept as calm as possible since nervous frightened cows produce milk of lower quality; for example, their panicky reaction to the parasitic warble flies in summer can be reduced by providing shade and water where the flies don't go. Special attention to thorough milking is essential as the last of the milk may have a butterfat content ten times that of the first. When my uncle had inexperienced milkers he would go round and finish off or 'strip out' each cow himself. Time of milking is very important too: ideally this should be twice a day at equal intervals of every twelve hours, but this makes a long day for the farmer. Uncle got close to this by starting milking at five o'clock in the morning and again about four o'clock in the afternoon, making eleven and thirteen hour intervals. The milk from the longer period contains less butterfat than that from the shorter. Intervals of sixteen and eight hours are inviting trouble with quality and would be viewed unsympathetically in the courts in a case of prosecution for substandard milk. Perhaps it is understandable that those cider drinkers relaxed a bit in the middle of the day.

So, having done their best and with a simple faith in British justice, the farmers converged each morning on the milk factory. It was rather like a medieval market day, but every day.[24] From miles around and from all directions horse-drawn carts and old cars and tractors (all classics now, and some even then) towing trailers carried their clanking milk churns. When we were young the trip to the milk factory was a treat, for the factory was fascinating. We drove along slowly at about twenty miles per hour; this was quite normal: most lorries were limited by law to thirty miles an hour and the larger ones to twenty. The pace of life was different: over thirty miles an hour in a car was considered excessive; this was just as well since most vehicles had only cable brakes whose stopping powers were rather less than that of a modern handbrake. We passed or met many other farmers on the way, identifiable from a distance by their idiosyncratic vehicles; our mutual yet perfunctory acknowledgements symbolised a sense of shared achievement – 'Yes, I've done my bit'. For a long time after the war Britain continued to take a patriotic pride in its food production.

The factory itself, at least the part we saw, was like a slow cartoon parody of the slick and speedy bottling plants of today. Once the milk had been checked the churns were slid onto a narrow ramp of rollers and from there a crude but ingenious machine took them over completely. At frequent intervals a chain would descend around the rear churn and the whole line would be slowly chivvied in a crowd, up and along the ramp, each churn wobbling and rattling and banging against the next one and it seemed almost that they were saying, 'Don't push me, I can't go any faster!' The whole operation was driven by steam power and noisy jets of steam squirted out apparently at random from safety valves and occasionally, with a loud exciting roar, an enormous cloud of steam would envelop everything and everyone on the platform.

At the top of the ramp the churns entered a large wheel and one by one were tipped up and the contents poured out into a tank. They then mysteriously entered through a large canvas flap into a hidden area where they were mechanically washed and sterilized by superheated steam; although we couldn't see we could hear bangs and crashes and more jets of steam and would not have been surprised to hear screams. The lines of churns then emerged, upside down to drain, on another ramp, going down this time. They were then flipped upright and slid rapidly down the ramp to crash with more loud bangs into churns waiting at the bottom. Down a separate little curving ramp came the heavy lids, also washed and sterilised; at the bottom stood a man whose

job was to place a lid on each churn. He then
expertly slid the churns across to a waiting area
where the farmers could pick up the next day's
supply. The whole operation was extremely noisy
with rattling chains, clanking machinery, banging
churns and above all the noisy steam so that it
was difficult to talk without shouting. We stood in
the safety of the trailer to watch and we loved it.

I took on a different attitude to all this when,
having passed my driving test, I was asked
occasionally to take the milk to the factory on
my own. The old pre-war Austin 10 had by now
been replaced with an Austin 'Somerset' model,
one of the most attractive production cars ever
made; its rounded design had an overall balance
and unity from the front to the very end which
few cars achieve. All the cars that were on the
roads in those days are of course classics now and
the lorries are antiques; although they weren't
thought of then in that way, they nevertheless had
an intriguing individuality of character and a sort
of humanity that few if any cars show today, for
although those old cars were mass produced, the
designs still had their origins in craftsmanship. As
I drove, it was important that I should be ready to
recognise and acknowledge the vehicles of all my
uncle's friends and acquaintances so that I should

not be thought 'offish', for all these details were noted in village life with little allowance for error. I knew however that the real problem would arise when I reached the factory.

The reception platform at the factory was a long structure set at the height of the cargo bed of the company's lorries. Vehicles delivering churns backed up to the platform end-on and it was long enough to accommodate about a dozen vehicles in this way. Backing a trailer attached to a car is a particular skill and I had not had much practice then. Sometimes it goes very well and looks easy, but sometimes it just doesn't go right and the trailer will suddenly flip to one side. I often backed tractors and trailers on the farm, but that was different: they were longer and so less skittish; there was plenty of space; there was nothing expensive to hit; I could take my time; I wasn't surrounded by impatient people all jostling for a place; I had a good view of what the trailer was doing from the open tractor; it didn't matter whether the tractor and trailer were in line as long as the trailer ended up in the right position; and above all there was no audience.

In front of the platform was a huge, plain concrete-surfaced plaza and I had to swing into this and back a long way up to the platform knowing – or feeling anyway – that everyone would be watching to see how I made out; certainly they would take notice if I got it wrong, just as people do when someone is berthing a boat. I hoped that I might be lucky and that there would be plenty of room at the platform, but when I arrived there was only one space. I would like to have paused for some vehicles to leave, but there were others waiting impatiently behind me. Experienced drivers appear to back vehicles almost instinctively and at speed; the timed tractor and trailer driving competitions at agricultural shows are fascinating to watch, but maybe it will look so easy that unless you have tried it yourself you may not appreciate and enjoy the display of skill. Concentration had to compensate for lack of practice, so I concentrated hard, took it slowly and managed to get the trailer into the space without hitting the vehicles either side. Of course no one took any notice.

On the platform all seemed pandemonium. Each driver lifted his churns up on to the platform, gathered them together and guarded them like a sheepdog until a busy checker came along to measure the depth of milk and take samples from the churns. An experienced farmer would watch this procedure carefully. Cream of course rises to the top of the milk; to take a proper sample the milk must be mixed thoroughly. But the checker seemed just to swish his dipper around a couple of times before lifting it out. If he plunged it deeply and brought it up swiftly then he would get watery milk, but if he dipped just the top he would get creamy milk. I didn't argue. The checker entered details in a rolled-up notebook and then wrote the number of gallons in each churn on its respective label, tore it off the churn and handed the labels to me as receipts. Against the deafening background noise of the machinery we could only communicate by nods and gestures. He then rolled or slid the churns on to that fascinating machinery and hurried off to the next cluster. I collected five clean and empty churns, dropped them into the end of the trailer and quickly drove away and home to breakfast. I had a feeling only of relief and did not allow myself any hubristic satisfaction on this occasion; there is a thing well-known as 'beginner's luck' and I would have to do it all again sometime.

☙10 Boundaries ❧

Agriculture is the cultivation of the fields, from the Latin word *ager*, a field. A field implies boundaries. In medieval times the boundaries of the open fields were, as the name suggests, often transient and were not physical barriers. It is thought that areas set aside to be cut for hay were fenced off temporarily, although we don't know how exactly this was done; presumably with hurdles or with the rough sort of fence which we still made sometimes. A process of enclosure of fields with permanent barriers of banks, hedges, ditches or walls has gone on since Iron Age times and each period – Iron Age, Roman, Saxon, Medieval, Tudor and eighteenth century – has produced its characteristic features. The great wave of enclosures and privatisation of common land in the eighteenth century allowed advances in cultivation and stockbreeding which enabled Britain to feed its growing urban population.

A man who received land under an enclosure award was legally obliged to fence it in some way; a farmer is still required to keep his own stock from straying onto a neighbour's land, but the

neighbour is not expected to have to keep them
out. In most lowland areas this fencing was
done with hawthorn hedges; on the Somerset
Levels with their high water table the universal
boundaries were the ditches. These were not the
little drainage gutters such as we commonly see
beside roads; a few were like small rivers – some
were rivers, but all were substantial and in them
the water slowly and quite imperceptibly flowed
to the sea. I don't know what the total length and
volume of this drainage system might be. In the
1930s an eminent professor of geography tried
to estimate the total length of field boundaries
in England. He worked out the average size of
the fields from the detailed information kept by
the Ministry of Agriculture; he then assumed
an average shape – and hence an average length
of boundary – for every field and multiplied the
estimated boundary by the total number of fields.
After he had published his results he realised that
since nearly every field shares a boundary with its
neighbour he had over-estimated the total length
by about a factor of two. Even great minds can
make simple errors it seems. What interests me
more is how much human effort was necessary to
enclose a field with a boundary ditch.

Before the period of comprehensive enclosure

of the moors in the eighteenth century, piecemeal and isolated enclosures had been made. Some of these have Saxon names and are usually presumed to date from that time, although it should be remembered that the common people continued to speak Anglo-Saxon after the Norman-French conquest; indeed they never ceased to speak it until it again became the language of England in Chaucer's time. Thus the peasants who tended the animals used the Saxon names for them, which we still use: pig, sheep and ox, while the Norman rulers who enjoyed the luxury of eating the meat used the French words: *porc, mouton* and *boeuf* which we know today as pork, mutton and beef. My uncle rented a field called Leverham. 'Hamm' is an Old English or Saxon name that indicates a water meadow or enclosure near a stream; 'lever' means it was a place where rushes grew. Could this field have been a Saxon enclosure? We don't know. Hamm incidentally has often later been shortened to ham which, confusingly, means a village.

To get to Leverham we first took a short cut through the barton or farmyard of the farmer opposite, the one with the cider-drinkers. We then had to go past his large pond which was the home of a flock of plump, white, domesticated geese.

Always two or three ganders broke away from
their apparently peaceful preening and paddling
and rushed aggressively towards us, wings
flapping and necks and beaks outstretched, hissing
in their alarming way. This was quite scary when
I was young and small, but as I became older I
soon discovered that if I seized one by the neck,
just behind his head, he was helpless and his anger
soon subsided, whereupon they all swaggered back
to the pond, muttering to each other. They had
made their point. We carried on down the length
of the farm's home ground and then crossed one
of the ancient green lanes through a pair of gates
into an old orchard with huge, decrepit, yet still
prolific, cider-apple trees. This was known as
Fudge's Orchard. Fudge was an old man who had
lived there an unknown time ago and there in the
corner were the now meagre ruins of his cottage.
We were always told that Fudge's Orchard was
exactly one acre in size, which gave us a sort of
yardstick to judge areas. Turning left through the
orchard we next came out into a long narrow field
called Leg Ground, or more precisely Binning's
Leg Ground since it once belonged to a farmer
Binning. This term 'leg' was always used for such
narrow fields which seemed somehow to have
been leftovers from the pattern of enclosures. We

always thought the term was descriptive of the long narrow shape, but I discovered later that *'leg'* is an old Anglo-Saxon word for island, which may be significant. For along one side of this leg was a major drainage channel, dignified by a simple hand operated sluice which controlled the water levels in surrounding fields, although I never saw a diference in level either side of it of more than a few inches. Might this channel once have been a meandering stream, straightened during the enclosures? If so, Leverham may well have been a rushy or reedy enclosure or watery meadow first identified in Saxon times.

Leverham itself as we knew it was about four acres in size and its square shape suggested an eighteenth century origin. However, old maps show Leverham as having been a much larger irregularly shaped enclosure and it appears to have been subdivided at some time, for the remaining parts have modern and unimaginative names such as Orchard Ground, which had a little orchard attached to it, and Square Ground. In some adjacent fields a similar subdivision seems to have taken place; old legal documents in my possession show that a small triangular field of about three acres called Stone Mead is a remnant of a larger enclosure of that name, which other sources show as mentioned in a document of 1583; again the other part is now named prosaically as Six Acres. There are no stones in the clay soil and the name Stone Mead possibly refers to a large medieval parish boundary stone in an adjoining field called Stone Post, which I regret to say I sold a few years ago.

Meanwhile on the south of the village and on the edge of the moors we had a little field of three and a half acres known as Milking Plot which seems to have been an isolated enclosure formerly. One can imagine the cattle being brought in each evening from the open moors to be milked in the safety and convenience of the milking plot.

'The lowing herd wind slowly o'er the lea.'

Fields of this size – three to four acres – were fairly common; it was said to be the area which a small team of mowers using scythes could cut in a day. However, I have read in old farming books that a team of three men could mow ten acres in a ten hour day. Perhaps more significantly, it was the area of hay which could conveniently be handled in a few days of fine weather using traditional methods. The cows would get much of their nutrition from the moors; their dung would bring those nutrients to the milking plot which in turn might be temporarily given over to hay production in spring and early summer.[25]

How much effort then was involved in digging the large ditch around Milking Plot? At first sight it seems a daunting task. However, a little arithmetic shows that a square of three and a half acres would have sides of 130 yards and a total perimeter of 520 yards. If a ditch was dug two yards wide and one and a half deep the volume of the ditch would be 1560 cubic yards. Modern estimates of building work assume a man can dig out a cubic yard in about three hours. Working nine hours a day and six days a week, which was not unusual, two men should be able to do the job in forty-three weeks or four men in about twenty-two weeks. In short, it could be done in a single summer, which was much less time than it would take to establish a quick-thorn hedge. The total drainage system of the Levels, however, had been the work of centuries.

We had some experience of this work because in order to maintain these ditches they had to be dug out or 'thrown' by hand, which we did in summer when the water was low. We were grateful that the soil contained no stones to interfere with our digging, but as we approached the water-table another difficulty arose; the clay soil became very sticky and it wouldn't slide off our spades as we attempted to throw the material out of the ditch. This slowed the work down considerably and the unexpected jerk could easily 'rick' our backs as we swung the spades around while our feet were still stuck in the mud of the ditch bottom. A trick my uncle showed me was to wet my spade each time before I dug by quickly dipping it into the water, after which the clay would slip off easily and the work went on very well. Over time, shrubs and trees had grown up along the banks of many of the smaller ditches, whether by nature or by human intervention I don't know; but the larger strategic drains or 'rhines' were mostly kept clear of vegetation to avoid blockages and so that they could be maintained by machines more easily. These rhines were the responsibility of the drainage authorities; it was the smaller ditches that were regularly thrown by hand by the farmers and then usually only the short stretches where there were no hedges. These lesser ditches, however, made up by far the largest part in terms of total length.

From time to time some progressive farmer would have a complete ditch around a field re-cut by a mechanical excavator. This involved, first, the removal of all hedges and trees from the banks, which my mother always lamented; in this, as in other attitudes, she was often ahead of her time. That mysterious world of light and shade; of half-seen twittering and rustling birds; of butterflies and blackberries, and of waterside flowers: all that we understood as a hedge, quite destroyed. The machine used to do the digging was correctly called a drag-line: a large rectangular iron scoop or bucket hung down on a retractable cable from the upper end of the arm or boom of a sort of crane. This bucket was attached also to the front of the body of the crane by another, horizontal, cable which too was retractable. With an upward movement of the mechanical arm the operator could sling the bucket forward and by letting go the vertical cable at just the right time the heavy bucket sliced down the side of the ditch. Then the bucket was pulled, dripping with water and full of mud, inwards and upwards by the cables, while at the same time the whole machine was rotated to dump the mud at its side. To get the edges of the ditch straight and smooth in this way was skilled work requiring judgement, much more so than the operation of the precision-controlled hydraulic diggers of today, and therefore so much more interesting to watch. Sometimes the operator would realise the bucket was going to drop at the wrong distance and would haul it in rapidly before it did so, but this was unusual. As a young boy I was happy to watch this working marvel for hours; also it had caterpillar wheels: like a tank! Having dug as much as possible within the arc of its jib, the machine, ponderous and lurching on its tracks, moved to a new position to start another section. This was a spectacle worth waiting for.

All this digging was intended to improve the drainage of the ground by lowering the level of the underground water in the soil. This in turn discouraged unproductive plants such as wet-land rushes and encouraged the more nutritious grasses.[26] Drier, warmer soil meant also that the grass grew earlier in the spring. Even so, it is debateable whether the farmer would get an economic return from the cost of the operations, but this was not a concern since the government provided generous grants as part of a national programme of agricultural improvement. For maximum benefit another operation known as mole draining was often carried out as well. A mole drainer is a metal frame mounted on skids; underneath the frame there is a large vertical knife and on the lower end of the knife is a large bullet-shaped piece of metal, several inches in diameter – the 'mole'. The mole is started against the bank of the ditch and the frame is pulled across the field by a wire cable operated by a winch on a tractor or on a steam engine, as in steam ploughing. The narrow slit cut in the soil by the knife soon closes up, but the tunnels made below by the mole stay open for several years and act as very effective drains. The spacing and depth of the drains are matters of experience, depending on the capillary properties of the soil, and it was always said that land drainage was as much an art as a science. All these complex and expensive operations had of course one simple purpose: to grow more grass.

Hawthorn or 'quick-thorn' – so called because it grows into a hedge quickly – was by far the most dominant species in our hedges. There were also blackthorn, some goat willow or pussy willow, whose inflorescences are like small soft cat's paws, the wild rose or dog-rose and many, many brambles or blackberry plants. The only woodland timber tree which grew successfully on the heavy clay was the English elm and rows of these giant and harmonious trees here and there along field boundaries dignified the countryside around the village; their irreplaceable loss to disease in the 1960s was a great impoverishment of the scenery – imagine, for example, Constable's painting 'The Cornfield' without those large trees beside the lane. Ash trees, on the other hand, are most particular where soil is concerned and they grew very poorly in the wet soil. I only knew of one oak tree in the whole village and, except in private gardens, there were none of the viburnums, nor any hazel, holly, dogwood, buckthorn or elder, which are so common elsewhere in the country.[27]

Across England records have survived that show when many boundaries were first established. Some decades ago two biologists, Pollard and Hunter, showed a remarkable correlation between the age of any hedge and the number of species in it and that this relationship could be used to establish the age of a hedge; where the correlation did not work there was usually a good historical explanation. Essentially each species represents one hundred years and it might be thought therefore that our hedges were quite old. However, the technique requires random samples of thirty-yard stretches and as the secondary species in our hedges were infrequent I would guess from memory that most hedges were 'two-species' hedges: that is, hawthorn plus one other. This suggests that the hedges were about two centuries old, but since the enclosures were made by digging they could well have been much older than the hedges; certainly it is known that some of the main drainage channels were made under the management of the Abbots of Glastonbury long before the Reformation of the sixteenth century.

As explained earlier, dairy country is traditionally untidy and on the whole our hedges were much neglected, especially on the smaller farms. On the other hand, in dairying areas hedges provide useful shelter for animals against wind-chill, especially in winter – for cold animals produce less milk; and so it was that fields around the farms generally had tall hedges whereas the summer pastures on the moors had few. The hawthorn has another property, which is not unique however, that allows it be nearly severed close to its base and the live stems 'laid' over at a shallow angle when they will continue to live and grow – perhaps another explanation for the appellation 'quick' in the biblical sense of 'alive' – to make a barrier against animals, especially sheep. Hedge laying is an ancient practice and Julius Caesar describes how the Gauls were making their hedges in this way at least two thousand years ago.

Since we kept no sheep, the thorn bushes were mostly allowed to grow to their full size of fifteen feet or more. Although occasionally a large limb might be bent down to fill a gap, there was no tradition of laying hedges properly and neatly as there was in arable and sheep farming areas and which now, pleasingly, is being revived; indeed it was regarded as something of a mystery. While a wide ditch or a thick growth of thorn, even when not laid, would keep the cows in the grounds, hedges were in fact often gappy and many minor ditches, especially those under the hedges where maintenance was difficult to carry out, were silted up. The jarring truth which I am reluctant to tell is that everyone used barbed wire. Without this economical and convenient material the maintenance of all those boundaries would have been impossibly labour intensive and costly for a small family farm.

After early experiments, barbed wire was patented by a man from Ohio in 1867. It consists of one, two or more strands of steel wire with small, sharp, metal points attached. Its influence on farming in the dry open grasslands of the United States was similar to that of the enclosures in England, although at a much larger scale.

It would be interesting to know how, in economic terms, boundaries on the Levels were maintained before barbed wire: how many men were employed on this and by whom; were hedges properly laid then; how were the banks of the ditches protected from animals? Certainly labour had been cheap in the past. Casual labourers might work for no more than a simple meal, a bed of hay in a barn and, usually, cider. They were the fortunate ones. This diet could be supplemented by a wide range of items foraged from the hedges and ditches themselves, and in too many cases that might be all that they had. There are stories of labourers found dead beside the road with nothing but sour dock in their stomachs. William Cobbett, in his *Rural Rides* notes frequently the starvation conditions of the English farm labourers in the first part of the nineteenth century.

In the winter or early spring I would undertake to go around all the boundaries of certain grounds in my spare time and put them in order. The first thing was to cut back encroachments from the hedges into the pasture, for our tall hedges were in effect linear woodland; grassland in England is always seeking to revert to forest. The story of much of England over centuries is of people making clearings or 'assarts' from the wild wood to create pasture or arable land. This is not strictly true of the Levels which have been reclaimed from the sea, but as long as they are protected from the waters they too will try to become forest. I would find that suckers and seedlings of hawthorn and blackthorn had grown up within a yard or so of the hedge-line. Most rapacious and tangled of all were the tough fast-growing runners of brambles which arched down from their place in the hederows and took root in the grass. Everything had to be cut right down flush with the soil, for a single stump overlooked could break the mowing machine in summer and waste a day's mowing at least. Then the hedge itself as high as I could reach was trimmed back to its line to allow free passage of the tractor. The best tool for most of this work was like a straight billhook with a long wooden handle so it could be used with two hands; it was called a 'slasher' which indicates exactly how it was used. The more accurately I could hit the right spots at the best angles with just the appropriate amount of force the quicker the job was done. Slash at right angles to the wood and it will just move away; slash at a long shallow angle and the wood remains attached by a long untidy split: somewhere between these extremes will be just right to cut through small branches with one satisfying blow. It was pleasant, healthy work.

Using the hooked blade of the slasher turned upwards the lighter material was dragged into heaps and burned in the fields. Playing with fire was always satisfying, from the initial faltering success in lighting to the loud and rapid crackling as a new load of branches burst into flame on the established hot bed of ash. Control of fire distinguishes us from all other animals. Fire, a good servant and a bad master uncle often said, which was a warning not to be careless, for hedges are full of dry grass and dead leaves and can take light and burn fiercely, maybe leading on to hayricks and even to houses. He always hated to see good grassland destroyed under our bonfires; the areas of our fires were small, but the scars took years to heal.

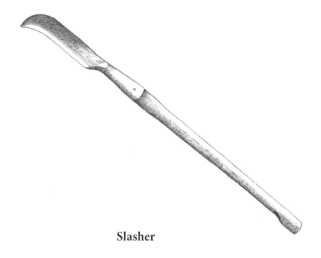

Slasher

This work was not done only to maintain the hedges as boundaries; it was done to protect the grassland from the forest in the centuries-old way. The function of those boundaries was to enable the grassland to be exploited as a great milk producing machine and I now had to inspect the existing barbed wire fences. Was the wire rusting away, was it slack or even broken, and were the posts rotten? The barbed wire was fastened to posts or, more controversially, to trees, with large wire staples hammered in. If the wire was slack the staples were loosened with a special tool and the wire strained tight with a claw behind a barb and refastened. New posts were cut from the hawthorns in the hedge itself or from a withy tree and hammered into the soil. With the boundaries in order, the ground was now ready for harrowing and later for grazing or mowing.

Barbed wire is controversial for two reasons. First, old wire becomes embedded invisibly into the trees as they grow; then when the timber is converted at the saw-mills the hidden metal damages the huge saw blades and a day may be wasted on their resharpening. This possibility of embedded wire in hedgerow trees reduced their market value. In the days of small scale enterprises, hedgerow trees were an important source of timber for the nation; up to a third of the country's oak trees were reckoned to be growing in hedgerows rather than in forests. The equivalent proportion of elm trees must have been much higher, for elm woodlands were rare. Good hedgerow timber was traditionally a valuable personal asset for a farmer, too, since he could always sell a few trees when cash was short.

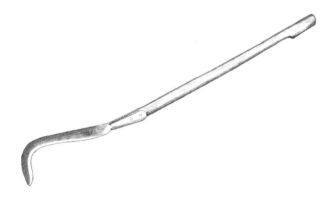

Another style of Slasher

Timber merchants and boat builders sent their horse drawn pole-wagons far out into the country to bring home huge trees of oak or, as in our case, elm. I knew one retired carter quite well and he told me that he often had to work many hours in a day at this work since the journeys were long and slow. I still have his old brass-bound fleam, used in the dubious practice of medicinal bleeding of sick horses. In fact we used his old pole-wagon, painted in the firm's cheerful colour of canary yellow, which had been cut down in length and converted for work on the farm. My woodwork master taught us that it was a very irresponsible action to fasten wire to trees. He liked to show us a specimen log which had been split open to show the wire and a staple inside; by a rough counting of the tree rings he worked out that the wire had been first attached to the tree about fifty years before it was felled. As I worked I imagined his disapproving presence and always removed and refastened the wire to the elm trees so it never did grow in, but whether there was already wire inside from perhaps fifty years ago I had no idea; the much more frequent hawthorns were never sent to the mills anyway.

The second problem with barbed wire concerned the hunt. Riders like to go willy-nilly wherever the quarry leads and they hate barbed wire which they reasonably regard as very unsporting since it is very difficult to see and may seriously injure a horse or even a rider.

There had been no tradition of hunting in the locality, for it was not that sort of society, until that is a hunting family moved in from 'down-country'

– a land of squires. Our lands, however, were not managed for hunting; the boundaries were not the neat, narrow hedges, walls and banks of typical hunting country where barbed wire was usually proscribed. That type of landscape belongs to large agricultural estates and compliant tenant farmers. Most of our hedges were much too tall to be jumped or too wide, as were many of the ditches. Some people said that the new family had brought the foxes too, which was not impossible, and that there had been no problem with foxes previously. I have a vivid mental picture of the bloody destruction wrought one night by a fox in my mother's hen-house: a dozen hens with their heads bitten off; not for food, but in sheer blood lust. At first, however, the hunt went after hares: a lot of stout farmers' sons rushed around in less-than-stylish clothes on rather less-than-stylish horses in all directions, for a hare does not run straight as a fox often does and I sometimes saw the hare lolloping along in quite the opposite direction. All this activity seemed greatly out of proportion to its immediate objective, which was after all only a sort of large rabbit. My mother thought the whole thing rather ridiculous and she was in any case opposed to the hunt. The countryside was uniformly flat and the small fields, which often were dangerously waterlogged in winter, were all enclosed with hedges and ditches; there was no rough open land suitable for a good chase and the riders mainly looked around for field gates to go through. It just was not natural hunting country.

Hares in any case are the least harmful of animals, except perhaps to each other when they engage in their mad boxing matches in spring or chase each other helter-skelter across the fields. They can run at speeds of over forty miles per hour and so are a good match for a horse, but they can't maintain this speed for long. Their low numbers mean they are no threat to growing crops and grass, unlike their prolific rabbit cousins, although when hares are hungry in winter they may damage small fruit-trees. Their supposed association with magic has been widely believed for centuries and there was something magical when we were children in seeing these rather rare animals at their unusual games on a spring evening.

Some hedges, usually those alongside roads or near to farms, were regularly trimmed low in a more conventional and tidy manner. The tool for this was a 'staff hook' which had a blade rather like a sickle or reaper's hook and a very long handle. It couldn't cut such big stuff as could

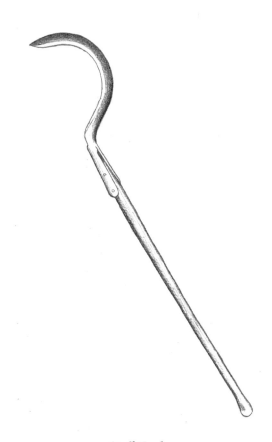

Staff Hook

the slasher, but it was more suitable for dealing with regular young growth. Most people rode bicycles in those days and if there was not to be an outbreak of punctures in the village I had to be careful to keep the road clear of the thorny hedge trimmings. This was not easy, for a single small thorn overlooked could puncture a tyre. Riders approached the scene of my work suspiciously and made a point of riding on the opposite side of the road as though I had the plague.

From time to time I repaired or replaced ('rehung') field gates. These were mostly made of local oak or sometimes of imported pitch pine brought in by the small wooden sailing ships which were still to be seen lining the wharfs of local rivers. Heartwood of oak, which has served its living purpose and in death has been stuffed with natural preservatives by the tree, is well-known to last for centuries. But the outer sapwood, although less durable, was still too valuable a timber to be discarded and our gates rotted eventually. Metal gates were becoming available then, but uncle argued that if a cow caught her leg in the bars – cows do strange things when panicked – it was much quicker to saw or even tear a piece out of a wooden gate; he was always thinking of the welfare of his cows.

I drove the car and trailer to a little timber yard about ten miles away situated on the edge of the hills and thus closer to the oaks. Set among trees, it was a simple, delightful place, scented with the solid tangy smell of sawn oak. The entrance led across a small yard, softly surfaced with the discarded bark and chippings of many years, straight into the only shed where the large motorised saw-bench stood. An overhead iron gantry with chain hoists could carry logs directly from the entrance to the saw. Around the yard were piles of tree trunks 'in stick'; that is, the logs had been sawn into planks of various thicknesses and these were now stacked up on top of each other with thin sticks between them to allow the air to circulate and dry the timber slowly and naturally: one year for every inch of thickness was the rule. A four inch plank would thus take four years or sixteen seasons of this treatment before it was ready for use; today timber is dried or 'seasoned' artificially in a few weeks in huge kilns, using large amounts of energy, because men are always in a hurry.

The yard employed two workers who did the sawing and stacking and one who made the gates. It seemed an attractive life to me then, but doubtless they had their problems of which I knew nothing. In one corner was the disused and crumbling saw-pit where whole trees formerly were sawn up by hand, which was unbelievably hard labour. Down in the pit, the huge trunk of the tree balanced on a beam over his head, one man provided most of the power, pulling the huge saw down through perhaps two feet of solid oak; sawdust rained on him throughout his working day. On top, standing on the trunk, the second man guided the cut and after each stroke had to drag the clumsy saw upwards again. They had to keep up this arduous task for many hours in a day's work. Even the motorized saw could do this heavy work only very slowly.

The yard supplied sawn timber to local wagon makers and coffin builders and the only things made there were the gates. Traditional farm gates were often called 'five bar' gates for they had five horizontal members, those at the bottom being a little closer together to deter the smaller farm animals; the top bar was stouter at four inches wide and was one more challenge for us to balance on and walk along as children. Every gate made of wood needs additional diagonal bracing of some form or its end will sag or 'drop' and drag on the ground – another natural lesson in mechanics. Each region had its style of field gates and these were of the Somerset variety: a symmetrical design of a diamond contained within an inverted W, which I always thought was the most beautiful. It had a sort of contented look. Uncle bought one nine-foot gate for exactly five pounds – a good week's wages – and an oak post and on the way home we dropped them off in the gateway of the Moor Ground.

Next morning promised one of those cold-warm bright days of mid-March, ideal for outdoor work. We spent a couple of hours digging out the old gatepost and putting up the new one: a fine length of nine inch square fresh oak which to anyone who loved timber as I did was a pleasure to work with. I knew too that under the weathered, grey, mossy surface of the old post there lay beautiful timber still, for it had rotted only at ground level, and my woodwork master delighted in showing us wood turnings and carvings made from discarded posts.

Unfortunately we had to destroy some of that old post to extract the gate irons. These irons were crude L-shaped pieces with a short, round, vertical peg to take the ring on the hinge of the gate and a longer horizontal spike which had to be hammered into the post. They were beaten out of red-hot iron by the village blacksmith and the simple design had not changed from medieval or even Roman times. Given that these irons were made of wrought iron which, except superficially, made them almost immune to rust, they were indefinitely reusable and I sometimes wondered how old they might be. The thick irons could not be driven directly into the hard oak until a hole had first been bored for them. This was outside my uncle's experience, nor did he possess the necessary tools, but I did, or rather my father did for woodwork was his hobby. The traditional tools would have been a simple centre-bit, as used by the ladder maker, or even a conical auger as used in making joints for timber framed buildings.

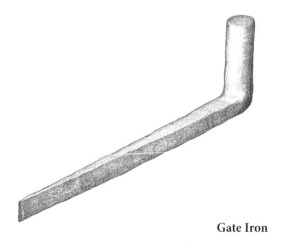

Gate Iron

I used a brace and a modern twist-bit. My father was reluctant I know to have his tools used in this way, but he was a generous person; however, he always impressed on me the need to pull back the bit frequently to clear the shavings so that it would not jam and break. It was so easy to turn the brace merrily and feel and smell the bit eagerly biting into the spicy timber when, suddenly, you could turn no more, neither forwards nor back and your bit was jammed. Too late!

We estimated the right height for the irons, leaving plenty of clearance under the gate for, as my grandfather reminded us, every wooden gate drops a little from new as the joints are stressed for the first time. I bored the holes diagonally on the corner of the post because, since the hinges were flat straps, only in this way could the gate swing through 180 degrees and so open either way, which sometimes was convenient. Then I hammered the irons in as uncle held the rammer against the other side of the post to absorb the shocks. Well before we judged the irons were right in we test hung the gate, for unlike modern metal gates the only adjustments possible were the angles and depths of the irons and it was impossible to move these once they were fully in. In fact we left a little spare so that in six months' time if the gate had dropped we could raise it by hammering the top iron in a little more. No longer would we have to lift and drag the old gate open and we had some excellent firewood, if the woodwork master didn't get it first.

Growing among the thorn trees in the hedges were thickets of brambles, dense and high, whose long, tangled, strong runners were very effective barriers to contain the cows. In the autumn these brambles carried generous crops of blackberries which were picked for sale. Women mostly, but also children and some retired men – indeed anyone who had some time to spare – spent long hours in the fields avidly picking these berries. The October weather was usually pleasant. A 'blackberry crook' cut from a small branch was used to pull down the runners into reach; children could pick the lower fruit. The black, juicy harvest was put into a small 'picking basket' which as it became full was periodically emptied into a larger container. Our hands became stained with purple juice as if in a wine harvest and bore light scratches all over from the bramble prickles. The cool, dark 'backhouse' of the farmhouse was fragrant with the scent of blackberries as each person's pickings accumulated in individual containers throughout the week.

The blackberry does not produce all its fruits at once, but considerately measures them out over several weeks. You may find every stage, starting from flowers to green, pink, black and dying fruits on one spray. Once a field had been 'picked-out' you waited a few days and there would be another flush of berries to be taken, but if you waited too long someone else might get them first. There was one very keen woman in particular who often got in before everyone else; this annoyed my grandmother greatly, but even if she owned the field she would never complain for, as explained previously, these berries seemed to be held 'in common'.

Blackberry picking was quite an industry in a small way. Once or twice a week a buyer in a van came round, stopping at houses which he knew had berries for sale. One person could accumulate large volumes in a good week and a variety of containers would be waiting for the 'blackberry man' who would weigh the fruits on a large squeaky spring balance with a huge brass dial which hung in the back of his van. He first weighed our containers full and then emptied the blackberries into one of his large bins and weighed the containers empty, writing the differences into his notebook: an early lesson in scientific method.

He would patiently weigh separately the smaller amounts brought by children and give us our cash earnings directly – our first real wages – which made us feel very important. The blackberries were later sent off to be made into a well-known brand of blackberry jam.

I knew those field boundaries intimately from my childhood and they had such individuality that I think if you had taken me blindfold and set me down beside a hedge I would have known which field I was in when I opened my eyes. I knew where the wrens built their small mossy globes as nests and where the moorhens bent down a circle of leaves to make their little island home each year in the reeds, and where the wood pigeons carelessly built their platform nests with just a few twigs so that you could see their two white eggs from beneath. I and my companions considered it a challenge to climb every elm tree and to reach every crow's and magpie's nest, even if it meant forcing a way up a thorn tree and getting badly scratched. I knew the locations of the fairy rings where mushrooms appeared as if by magic overnight: the large flat field mushrooms and the little round white 'buttons' hiding in the grass, both good to be taken home and fried for breakfast on crisp autumn mornings. I knew too where the wild bees nested in an old willow trunk[28], though I never dared to take their honey, and where to find the best sprays of rose hips to decorate the pulpit at harvest time and the pussy willow flowers for Palm Sunday. I knew where the yellow flags grew and the purple loosestrife which makes such lovely rococo curves when placed in a vase.

The meadows were flower-rich, and I remember when very young wading chest-high through graceful silky grasses, white moonflowers and purple knapweed as clouds of colourful butterflies and white moths rose before me as in an old jigsaw picture. I knew the damp patches where the uncommon, delicate, mauve cuckoo flowers grew that flowered when the cuckoo returned, and the more plentiful cowslips which my cousin liked to thread together with knitting wool and make into sweetly-scented cowslip balls. But woodland flowers naturally were what botanists call 'infrequent' and could be found in only a few safe spots under hedges: wild violets and primroses in early spring, flowering before the sheltering trees became fully leaved.

In those days, before so much development had taken place, the waters were clear; indeed one old lady living in a remote cottage still drew her water supply from a nearby ditch. I knew where

the watercress grew and we could harvest it
and eat it safely then. Sitting by a grassy bank
I could see the sunlight glancing right down
through the transparent water into another
world where, among the tresses of pondweed,
crowds of minnows flitted along with tadpoles
and sticklebacks, to be caught with a jam jar on a
string and – with special patience – the rare prize
of a redbreast: a puffed-up male stickleback in his
spring colours like a miniature salmon. We took
our prizes home and made our own aquariums out
of old bath tubs with a little sand and a few stones
and pondweed and watched our fish swim around
in the sunlit water. When, after a week we tired of
this, we put them back in the ditches.

In the shallower ditches we built mud dams
and small harbours for our toy boats. It might
take a whole day for the water to build up just a
few inches behind a dam and then we breached the
dam and watched as the water moved in a leisurely
way through the gap; we knew then that truly
the water did flow to the sea. We would seal the
dam and wait for the water to build up again just
for the interest of seeing it flow. When we were
a bit older we roamed the fields in the summer
evenings looking for good ditches to jump, daring
each other to try wider and wider ditches until

everyone had fallen in and we individually wound our various ways home dripping-wet in the twilight.

✑11 Spring ✑

The cows had gone. The cowshed was silent.
Pale sunshine lit up the dusty stalls, for the sun
was still low in the sky, even at mid-day. A few
sparrows hopped around looking for hayseeds to
eat. In a month or so the swallows would return
to their mud nests among the rafters. There
is something about a deserted farm building
which powerfully, though indistinctly, speaks
to the imagination, more so even than does a
church or a castle: a feeling of things hidden in
time or unexpressed, or inexpressible. In castles
and churches time is linear and punctuated and
articulate; in farm buildings time is cyclical, mute
and anonymous and so is mostly unknowable and
without limit; we are aware only of a vibrant
cycle of life repeated over and over from time
immemorial, whose details we shall never know.
Even in the most ancient church, perhaps the
oldest thing is the migration of the swallow
nesting in its porch.

After the morning milking, as the pulsing
machine that controlled the rate of milking fell
silent with a final gasp and when all the churns

of milk had been wheeled out to the dairy, uncle went along the stalls untying the halters of each cow. This time, as they clattered out of the cowshed one by one, the cows were directed not to the home ground, but into the orchard. When they were all assembled, the orchard gate leading to the village street was opened and the anxious animals rushed out onto the road, instinctively bunching together yet jostling each other for precedence. They were going to be taken to a field about a mile away and they wouldn't come back to the cowshed until next winter.

In the previous summer such movements along the roads had been a familiar routine for the cows. As most fields were small, some as little as three acres, their grass could support twenty-five or more milk cows for only a week or ten days. Then the cows had to be moved to another field. Because of the scattered land ownership this usually meant taking them along public roads and as there were also many small farms these movements were a regular feature of village life during spring and summer. Everyone called this 'changing cows' although it was of course changing fields. Changing cows was often arranged for Saturday mornings, since children were very useful in this operation. I would arrive at the field gate just as milking was finishing. Part of the ritual was to cut myself a thin stick from any conveniently low withy tree growing nearby. I cut off the little side twigs with my pocket knife and peeled away the soft, moist, sweet-smelling bark to make a smart white stick which I swished self-importantly and experimentally as I waited.

One problem was that despite the well-known frequency of these movements people in the village would leave their large entrance gates open. I had to cycle ahead – 'ride point' as cowboys say – shutting any open gates if possible and, if not, standing guard until several cows had gone by; then, choosing the moment, on to the next gate. Generally, once the lead cows had passed, the rest were more anxious about keeping up with the herd than wandering off on their own, whatever the temptation, but occasionally, a cow decided that a particular garden looked desirable and popped in to sample it. Then I had to get her out quickly before the whole herd followed with results almost too embarrassing to think about. Whilst any damage would have been our responsibility, we felt that owners who left their gates open – and not all did – were rather thoughtless. Uncle cycled slowly along at the back of the herd to make sure every animal kept moving. Some stout farmers herded with an old car, meandering from side to side of the road, window down, one arm outside banging the door noisily. Others used dogs, but these 'cowdogs' had none of the aptitude or training of sheepdogs for crowd control; they just trotted along at the rear and the only initiative they showed was when occasionally they crossed the road to encourage a straggler. With my nimble bicycle I did a sheepdog's work. Putting a small boy to stop a large cow may seem rather an unequal contest, but I soon discovered that waving my arms and stick and shouting a loud deep-throated 'Arrghhh' generally gave me dominance. There have been several reports in the papers recently of walkers, usually accompanied by dogs, having been trampled to death by cows. Cows are curious creatures and they will often come running across in a most alarming way to investigate any stranger and then a sort of mob mentality can take over. One correspondent however, presumably elderly, said that as he was quite unable to run he waved his arms at the cows and they left him alone. Bulls though are quite different and should be treated with great caution by everyone.

Cows have a sort of pecking order, which we called a bossing order. This was not usually obvious in a field, but when the herd was walking at its natural pace along a road there was always a 'boss cow' out in front who 'hoked' away any who tried to overtake her; there was also a meek cow that was normally last. The rest took up more or less predictable positions in between. If this natural order was allowed to develop, the herd ambled along in a seemingly contented manner.

Motorized traffic fortunately was slow and infrequent in those days, but if a vehicle wished to overtake us I cycled along the strung-out herd, easily shooing the cows to one side of the road with a tap of the stick; a tap on the rear would make the cow run, which we did not want, but with a tap on the shoulder the animals moved over easily. The car driver, if not too nervous, followed through with no problem and a cheery wave. Some farmers, less patient, made their cows run with a dog snapping at their hocks. This bunched up the animals and made overtaking impossible; so they were just made to run faster which did not improve the situation much. But cows don't run for pleasure as horses apparently do. If you see a cow run it is probably running away from the warble fly; or maybe it is running at you to chase you away from its calf: in which case hope that you can run faster. A running cow is an agitated cow or even a panicky cow and agitated cows may do foolish things; they also produce less milk. Uncle did not like his cows to be agitated.

On arrival at the field which had been prepared for them the cows poured eagerly through the open gateway. They didn't gallop around to express their new freedom or roll on their backs as frivolous horses do, but immediately fanned out in all directions and got their heads down to the serious business of eating fresh grass which they had not enjoyed for many weeks. They frequently moved on a few yards at a time, sampling the choicest grasses or herbs, tails swinging contentedly.[29] We shut the gate and leaned on it for a while, enjoying the sight of grass and cows reunited. But there was more to it than that. Uncle used to point out that if you see a farmer leaning on a gate don't assume he is being lazy; he is watching his animals: cows that are listless or not eating, cows that are in calf or in season, cows that are lame or have a cough. Observation is an important part of a good stockman's work. For the present all seemed well.

Grass and fencing: the third need in the fields

was for water; this was especially important for the production of milk which, despite its nutritional value, is about nine tenths water. The fields were surrounded by ditches, but these were mostly inaccessible because of the hedges. In any case we didn't want the cows to drink from the ditches and so the banks were usually protected by barbed wire; for as a cow goes down to drink from a ditch her front feet push in and destroy the soft clay bank and in a short time the ditch silts up and needs to be thrown out again. Apart from the water those ditches had another, special, attraction for the cows; this was the locally abundant *Glyceria*, aptly named sweet-grass. Sweet-grass is formed, as are all grasses, of a series of interlocking tubes like an open telescope. If I pulled out the top tube, cut off the lower six inches and squeezed flat the soft end, it made a Pan-pipe. In truth the noise was not very sweet; it sounded like a duck. Whether it could attract or 'call' a wild duck I never discovered. But the grass tasted sweet even to me and the cows would make great efforts to reach it, pushing down the wire if it was slack or weak. Occasionally a cow fell into a ditch or became stuck in the thick mud. After a few brief attempts to get herself out she would give up the struggle and lie down with, I would

say, a look of embarrassment on her face; not
the shy, blushing sort of embarrassment, but the
'Don't I look stupid?' sort. What else could she
do? The suction of the mud can be very powerful
and I suppose in nature she would slowly starve.

It was a problem when a valuable cow was
'down'. Once down, a cow seemed to become
fatalistic and would make no effort to help herself
as we pushed and pulled and shouted. This was
one of the few occasions when I heard my uncle
swear and of the even fewer occasions when my
grandfather didn't chide him for it; but when my
grandmother was seen hurrying across the field
the swearing stopped, to be replaced by a dark
scowl. She brought a coil of long, thick rope. Uncle
tied one end round the cow's head and we all got
in line and pulled; with this encouragement the
animal at last made an effort and scrambled out
of the ditch. Showing no obvious sign of injury
or discomfort she walked off to join the herd. She
would be carefully watched for a few days. This
time, we hoped, no harm had been done.

There were, however, special places where the
animals could drink in relative safety. Many years
ago in every ground, usually in corners where
they would least interfere with mowing, shallow
ramps leading down to the water had been cut

into the banks of the ditches. These features were known as 'watering eyes' or simply as eyes. Here the cows did not get stuck, for the ramps were surfaced with solid layers of stone extending into the water. The nearest stone quarries were several miles away in the hills and the making of these eyes must have involved numerous long, slow journeys with horses and small carts – for stones are very heavy – before motor transport became available. These journeys would have been shortened a little by the use of small coastal vessels which carried their cargoes of stone into local rivers.

The ramps had enclosing banks each side and were just wide enough for two cows to drink together, but in practice only one cow could drink at a time for it had to be able to turn around when it had finished. The animals took it in turn to break off from their grazing to go to drink; whether there was in fact a 'bossing order' in this I never noticed, but there was seldom any queuing or barging.[30]

For children these eyes made good 'camps'. Each side were the banks and many were over-arched with trees and dense bushes darkening the water and creating mysterious shady tunnels. I have an early memory of sitting by one of these eyes on a summer evening with my mother and using a piece of string on a stick to catch the fish-shaped willow leaves that floated on the water. In their shape and size willow leaves were just like the pictures of salmon on the labels of John West tins, which we used to cut out carefully and put to swim in jam jars of water; when the water was stirred the paper fish swam round and round very realistically.

Some years later I worked for a while on a farm high up on Dartmoor where I met 'Old Sid'. Sid was over fifty years old and lived with his mother. He was not very tall and his stance and his movements showed the stiffness produced by years of hard manual labour. Every morning, wearing his heavy farm boots, shiny leather leggings and an old gabardine raincoat, he took two hours to push his bike seven miles up the steep roads from the valley to the farm, arriving for work promptly at seven o'clock. After work he free-wheeled most of the way back down again, drank a pint of cider and went to bed. I never discovered any intellectual life in Sid, not even the clichéd wisdom of ordinary folk. He was not very good at most farm work and was extremely nervous on the occasions when the farmer was away and he helped me with the machine-milking.

Despite having worked in the country all his life he knew nothing of its wildlife. The idea of the countryman versed in nature's lore is largely a myth. Most knew nothing beyond the care of their own animals while a few had the knowledge necessary only to trap and kill. The American 'Fred' Law-Olmstead touring England as a young man in the 1840s said that he had never seen men so near the situation of brute beasts as the English farm labourer, and he had visited several European countries including Russia, although it should be said that the 'Hungry Forties' were a time of exceptionally bad weather, poor harvests and poverty in England. I most certainly would not describe Sid in that way, but perhaps it explains his origins. Born in 1898 he was scarcely two generations away from those hard times. Growing up as I had in a fluid society where Jack was as good as his master and had legitimate ambitions to better himself I had never met anyone like Sid. However, I did learn one useful trick from him, which impressed my uncle greatly when one day he again had a cow down.

Like the hedgehog of Archilocus, Sid knew one big thing: he was a champion hedger. He would never lack employment as long as his wizened body could keep working. Through autumn, winter and into spring he worked on the long-neglected and overgrown banks and hedges, helping to put the farm in order. There were no ditches on that upland farm and when the cattle wished to drink they wandered down the steeply sloping fields to the valley bottom and the small stream which was the boundary with the next farm. One day a cow was down, having slipped into the shallow icy stream and was in danger of becoming chilled and perhaps getting a fever; it was Sid who knew how to save the situation. He grasped one ear of the animal, put his mouth close and let out a fearful shriek. The cow leapt to its feet and ran off. It was the sort of occasion when even my uncle would have been happy to see his cow run.

Spring was the time when selected grounds were 'hayned up'. This meant that grazing stopped, the gates were closed and the grass was allowed to grow up tall to be made into hay. Hay should be made before or just as the grass begins to flower, for then the leaves and stems are most nutritious; after that stage the nutrients begin to be transported into the flowers and seeds and these are mostly lost in haymaking. Cereals, on the other hand, which have been bred over thousands of years from wild grasses, have been selected to retain their seeds after cutting, which for a wild plant would not be a good strategy for dispersal. Some old farmers had the idea that hay was best made as late as possible so that it was 'ripe before we cut it', but as science came to be applied to farming practices agricultural chemists showed there is a significant loss of nutrient value in just two or three weeks after flowering.

Hay is best made in early June which providentially is the time when the weather is usually most suitable. But we could make only a few acres at a time and so the haymaking had to be spread over several weeks. The grounds that were to be cut first were not grazed at all after the winter preparation, but others were eaten over once or twice and then hayned up in the hope that they would be ready a little later. As more and more grounds were set aside in this way during April and early May a feeling of expectancy grew over the country, a looking forward to the hectic and crucial, and to some extent still communal, period of haymaking in the summer.

It was considered a most unneighbourly thing to walk through a ground that was hayned up.

The grass was no longer a pasture over which animals roamed, but had become a crop which should not be damaged. In those days most farmers, though not all, tolerated people walking across their grounds; adults as well as children rambled fairly freely. We had all been to school together, or our fathers and mothers had, and jumped ditches, climbed trees and gone bird-nesting together. If anyone had hurt themselves while rambling they would never have thought of suing the farmer as might happen today, which is one reason farmers have become less friendly. We respected the 'Country Code': we didn't leave gates open, break down fences or drop litter that could injure or choke an animal. Trampling down the long grass in hayned up grounds led to tangled stems which blocked our simple mowing machines and in the past would have interrupted the smooth sweep of the mower's scythe. Regular walkers chose different routes, for just to be seen in a hayned up ground would invite disapproval and suspicion. But if, as part of our work or daily life, we had to go through a ground which had been set aside for mowing the rule was that we walked, in the tradition of Wellington's soldiers, carefully round the edges.

So where were the cows to go now, since so

many grounds had been closed up for haymaking? Out on the moors the land was drying out after the winter floods and offered lush grazing and plentiful water. These grounds were large rectangular eighteenth century enclosures of twenty, thirty or more acres and each one could provide grazing for many weeks; most farms in the village owned a ground or two on the moors for summer grazing. This where the cows would spend much of their summer.

I turned up near the end of morning milking on a Saturday morning as usual. It was one of those bright, still and misty days of early April, promising a fine day; the position of the sun in the sky showed only as a lighter patch in the silvery white vapour overhead. The distant ends of the fields and hedgerows were invisible in the white fog. No longer jostling, the cows plodded out through the gateway with the determined attitude and deliberate steps that people sometimes adopt when they are uncertain. After walking for a mile or so along a small road our procession crossed over the village street and we became aware of the road descending ever so slightly, perhaps only a few feet – but that was significant – and then as we rounded a sharp bend the landscape became suddenly and subtly different. Roads were straight, not meandering; changes in direction were right angles, not curves; hedges were less frequent and trimmed low; there were no big trees; ditches were wider and deeper, often dangerously so; grounds were much larger and there were very few houses. There was a delightful sense of spaciousness and the air was softer and sweeter; if we could have seen the blue sky above, it would have seemed huge as it was pulled out to the horizon by the long flat views in all directions.

We went around another bend and there ahead was our road: dead-straight and two miles long. At its end was yet another right angle corner and a very large ditch into which sometimes fast cars were driven when drivers failed to see the deceptive corner at night. The Paliamentary Commissioners, when they had laid out the enclosures in their rational geometric manner, had quite understandably failed to consider the requirements of fast cars. After a few years of accidents and after a few occupants had drowned, the council decided to put some red glass reflectors on posts in the road verge in front of the ditch. Even these did not give much advance warning and occasionally a car would drive right through them.

We, however, still moved at an old and different

pace, the cows now well strung out and keeping to the left-hand side of the road. Travelling in column or in convoy, or in a procession, seems to resonate with something in the human spirit, whether taking part or just watching. It is quite different from a crowd which is undisciplined and always on the edge of madness. It adds extra dimensions of meaning to any journey: cooperation, spatial coordination and shared progressive intent. Is it some folk memory of past migrations? Even the cows seemed to plod along purposefully, their breath condensing in the chill foggy air.

Gradually the mist brightened beautifully and then thinned; the sun was now a shining white disc with a precise circumference. Then, through the dimishing mist, across the fields on our right we glimpsed another parallel column moving through the pale sunlight in the same direction as ourselves. The animals were indistinct, but we could see their breath, too, rising into the mist. It was exciting to feel our ancient, shared purpose.

We were travelling on a metalled road; the column on our right was on an unsurfaced green lane. To our left and further away, we knew, was another metalled road; all three led directly to the moors. Then wonderfully, as the mist lifted even more, we saw on our left a third column emerge like a ghostly image on a developing photographic plate. It was a rare experience; for me it formed a unique and special memory: the three herds all moving at the same time through that timeless mist towards their summer grazing grounds. For that morning at least we were truly the Summer People.

NOTES

A little over two thousand years ago the Roman poet Virgil wrote a long poem known as the Georgics, after the Greek word *georgien* meaning to farm. While it has some political content, the main body of the poem is an explanation and celebration of farming practice. Then, over three centuries ago, Virgil's Georgics were translated into English by John Dryden. Dryden's translation helped to produce an attitude in England that farming was a desirable, even privileged, occupation worthy of the attention of aristocrats and even of kings, although for most people engaged in agriculture this pastoral ideal was far from the reality. When contemplating the continuity of agriculture, however, Virgil's words, although filtered through the mind of a seventeenth century Englishman and constrained by the poetic rules of rhyming couplets, still speak to us authentically over twenty centuries.

The numbers on the selected quotations below refer to numbers in the main text.

1
The soil exhaling clouds of subtle dews.

2
The sire of gods and men, with hard decrees,
Forbids our plenty to be bought with ease,
And wills that mortal men, inured to toil,

Should exercise with pains, the grudging soil.

3
Happy the man, who, studying nature's laws,
Through known effects can trace the secret cause.

4
… she [Tisiphone] strikes a universal blow:
To death at once whole herds of cattle go.

5
…where the soil, with fattening moisture filled,
Is clothed with grass.

6
… the genius of the soil…
with grass unbidden, decks the ground.

7
Nor must we pass untold what arms they wield,
Who labour…

8
No fences parted fields, nor marks nor bounds
Distinguished acres of litigious grounds.

9
The dikes are filled…
The rising rivers float the nether ground.

… a glut of gathered rain
The hollow ditches fills, and floats the plain.

10
His kine with swelling udders ready stand,
And, lowing for the pail, invite the milker's hand.

11
The various course of seasons must be found,
The weather and the setting of the winds.

12
Wet weather seldom hurts the most unwise;
So plain the signs, such prophets are the skies…
The swallow skims the river's watery face.

13
The farmer to full bowls invites his friends,
And, what he got with pains, with pleasure spends.

14
… apple-trees, whose trunks are strong to bear
Their spreading boughs …
Till with the ruddy freight the bending branches
groan.

15
But much more pleasing are those fields to see,

That need not ploughs…

16
If milk be thy design, with plenteous hand
Bring clover-grass…

17
Load with fattening dung thy fallow ground.
Earth manured, not idle though at rest.

18
New milk that, all the winter, never fails,
And, all the summer, overflows the pails.

19
… our homely sires…
Who filled the pail with beestings of the cow,
But all her udder to the calf allow.

20
…know that from the dam the worth of each
proceeds.
21
…these the laws
Imposed by Nature, and by Nature's cause.

22
… the blind laborious mole
In winding mazes works his hidden hole.

23

Some, cloven stakes; and (wondrous to behold!)
Their sharpened ends in earth their footing place;
And the dry poles produce a living race.

24

... the round year with daily labour fills.
And hence the country markets are supplied.

25

Next, fenced with hedges and deep ditches round,
Exclude the encroaching cattle from thy ground.

26

Though rushes overspread the neighbouring
plains.

27

Not every plant on every soil will grow:
The sallow loves the watery ground and low.

28

Nor bees are lodged in hives alone, but found
In chambers of their own ...
And in the rotten trunks of hollow trees.

29

The milky herds that graze the flowery plains.

30
Your lowing heifers, of their own accord,
At watering time will seek the neighbouring ford.
(Pastoral VII)

About the Author

Roy Preece grew up in the secret countryside of the Somerset Moors at a time when children could roam freely and safely over fields, farms and workshops. At age eleven he could put in a ten-hour day driving a tractor at hay-making. The brilliant headmaster of his traditional country grammar school had worked on radar research throughout the war, but after school was quite happy to put on overalls and feed the pigs which he kept to supplement the pupils' diet in the years of austerity.

The boys marked out the games pitches, put up the goal posts and even stoked the school boilers. Roy has since obtained degrees from three universities and spent most of his life as a lecturer, producing several books and a variety of articles, but he still believes in a self-reliant life and maintains this deeply felt practical side to his life by inventing, building, making furniture, and maintaining and sailing an old sail boat.